GIANT BOOK OF
MAZES

Roger Moreau

A Main Street Book

10 9 8 7 6 5 4 3

Published by Sterling Publishing Company, Inc.
387 Park Avenue South, New York, N.Y. 10016
Material in this collection was adapted from
Space Mazes © 1996
Great Explorer Mazes ©1997
Save the Earth Mazes © 1996
Jungle Mazes ©1997

This edition © 1999 by Sterling Publishing Inc.

CONTENTS

Space Mazes 5

Contents 7
Introduction 8
The Solar System Mazes 9
The Universe Mazes 34
Space Guides 47

Great Explorer Mazes 69

Contents 71
Early Explorers 74
19th-Century Explorers 84
20th-Century Explorers 92
Explorer's Guides 108

Save the Earth Mazes 133

Contents 135
Introduction 136
Oceans & Streams 137
Wildlife 147
Pollution 163
Help for Earth Savers 173

Jungle Mazes 197

Contents 198
Introduction 199
The Jungles of Central and South America 200
The Jungles of Africa 212
The Jungles of Southeast Asia 224
Jungle Guides 234

SPACE MAZES

Roger Moreau

Contents

Introduction 8
The Solar System 9
Solar System Information 10
Flight Plan Map 11
Space Shuttle 12
Space Station 13
Departure 14
Tour of the Sun 16
Tour of Mercury 18
Tour of Venus 20
Tour of Earth's Moon 22
Tour of Mars 24
Asteroids 26
Tour of Jupiter 28
Tour of Saturn 30
Uranus, Neptune and Pluto 32

The Universe 34
Trip to Andromeda 35
Planet with Life 36
Horsehead and Orion Nebulae 38
Exploring Star 40
Tour of a Black Hole 42
Spiral Galaxies 44
Returning Home 45
Space Guides **47**

INTRODUCTION

Mankind has set foot on and explored Earth's moon on several occasions, but no planet beyond it. Yet much has been learned about our solar system thanks to unmanned space probes that have landed on some of the planets and flown by others. Also, the Hubble space telescope has helped to broaden our knowledge of deep space. But for every question that has been answered, many new ones have arisen. If we are to learn more, someone must be found with the courage and determination to be the first to explore the rest of our solar system and beyond.

That someone is you!

Get ready to go on the most exciting adventures imaginable. Be prepared to leave this planet Earth via the space shuffle and dock at an orbiting space station. There you will board a single-seat star cruiser capable of speeds beyond that of light. Your itinerary will take you on a tour of our solar system and into the vast reaches of the universe.

So that you can successfully plan your trip, it is important for you to learn some basic facts about our solar system and deep space. This information can be found on page 10. Once you have studied these facts, carefully follow your flight plans and the rules regarding each destination you visit.

May you have a great trip and safe return!

THE SOLAR SYSTEM

The solar system is made up of a medium-size star we call the Sun, nine known planets and their moons, and asteroids and comets. The planets, their moons, and the asteroids and comets revolve around the Sun and are held in place by its gravitational pull.

The nine planets that revolve around the sun are classified as either inner or outer planets. The four inner planets—those closer to the sun—are Mercury, Venus, Earth, and Mars. Separating the inner and outer planets is a belt of asteroids. Asteroids are simply rocks that range in size from hundreds of miles in diameter to less than one. Beyond the asteroids are the remaining five outer planets—Jupiter, Saturn, Uranus, Neptune, and Pluto.

Of the nine known planets, only the inner planets have solid surfaces that a spacecraft could land on. Of those, Mercury has furnace-like temperatures because it is so near the sun. Venus, with an eternal cloud cover that causes a greenhouse effect, also has a sizzling surface temperature. Mars appears to be the most likely planet where human exploration might be possible. Most of the other planets are whirling balls of gas.

Fortunately, you will be equipped with a special suit that enables you to explore Mercury, Venus, Earth's moon, Mars, and the asteroids. To explore the other planets, you'll have to stay in your spacecraft.

THE SOLAR SYSTEM
Comparative size and order from the Sun

Sun
Size: 1,400,000 km
865,000 miles

Distance	Size

Mercury
57,900,000 km   4878 km
36,000,000 miles 3032 miles

Venus
108,200,000 km   12,100 km
67,000,000 miles   7,520 miles

Earth
149,600,000 km   12,756 km
93,000,000 miles   7,928 miles

Mars
227,900,000 km   6,787 km
141,500,000 miles 4,218 miles

Asteroids

Jupiter
778,300,000 km   142,800 km
483,700,000 miles 88,751 miles

Saturn
1,427,000,000 km   120,600 km
886,900,000 miles 74,953 miles

Uranus
2,870,000,000 km   51,800 km
1,783,000,000 miles 32,194 miles

Neptune
4,504,000,000 km   48,600 km
2,799,000,000 miles 30,205 miles

Pluto
5,900,000,000 km   3,000 km (?)
3,668,000,000 miles 1,865 miles (?)

Flight Plan Map

Find the path to each solar-system feature in order, from the Sun to Pluto. You can go underneath and over the top of each feature where indicated.

Space Shuttle

Board the space shuttle by following the correct fuel line to the ladders. Climb the ladders to enter the shuttle. You cannot go through any black partitions.

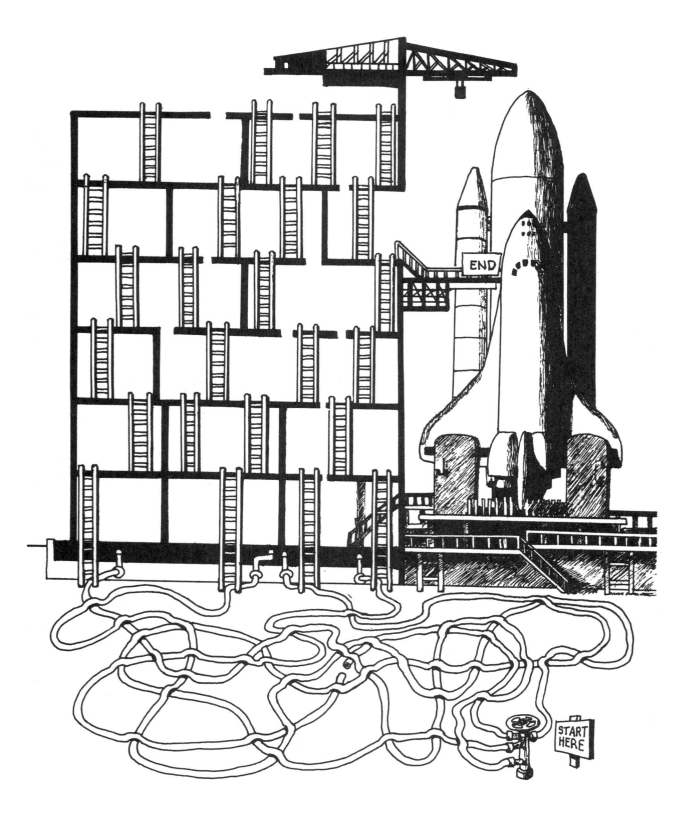

Space Station

Find a clear path to the distant space station, avoiding contact with any satellites.

Departure

This space station has not been completed, but the countdown has begun. You have 10

seconds to board the star cruiser. Find the right path to the cruiser. You can cross from one path to another by walking across the single planks. Hurry!

Tour of the Sun

Tour the Sun without burning up. To do this, stay on the white paths.

Tour of Mercury

Tour the planet Mercury. Once you leave the space cruiser, find a clear path around its

surface. Then return to the space cruiser. This place is pretty hot during the day, so you'd better hurry.

Tour of Venus

Molten lava is bubbling up all over the surface of Venus. Avoid the lava and explore the planet until you can find your way back to the space cruiser.

START

END

Tour of Earth's Moon

The surface of Earth's moon is filled with craters. Find your way between the craters and return to the space cruiser.

Tour of Mars

The largest known volcano in our solar system is Olympus Mons on Mars. Find a clear path to the top of the volcano and back to the space cruiser.

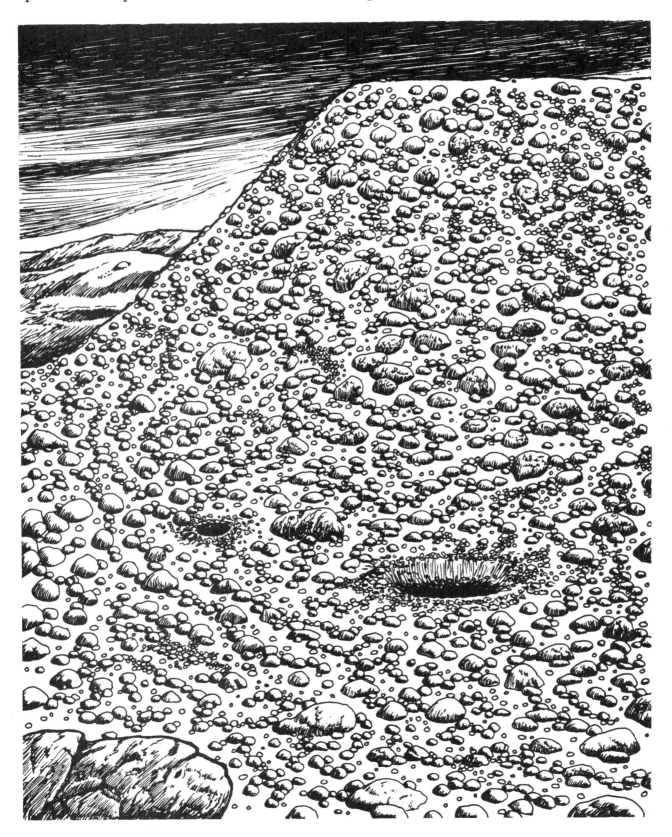

START · · END

Asteroids

Find your way from asteroid to asteroid and back to the ship. Travel only on the asteroids that appear to be touching each other.

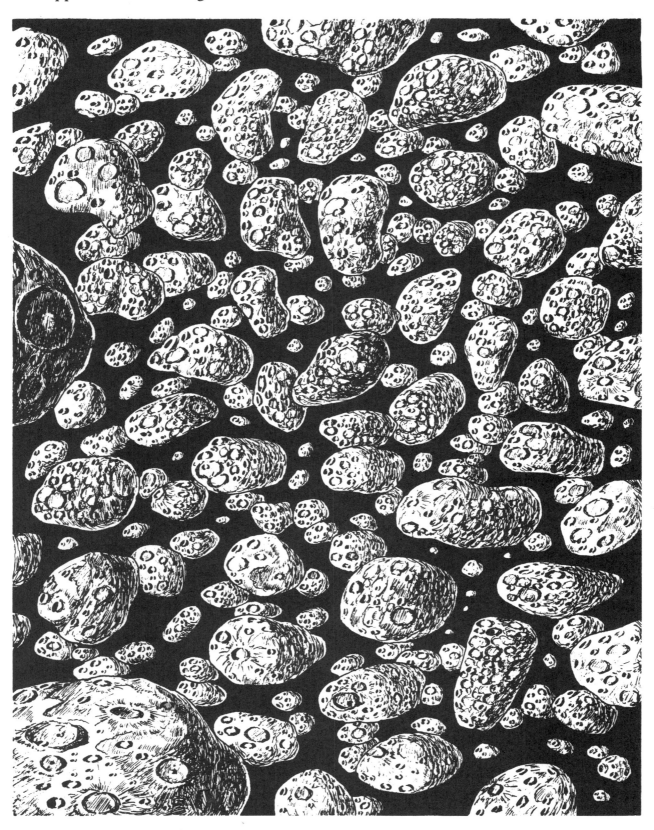

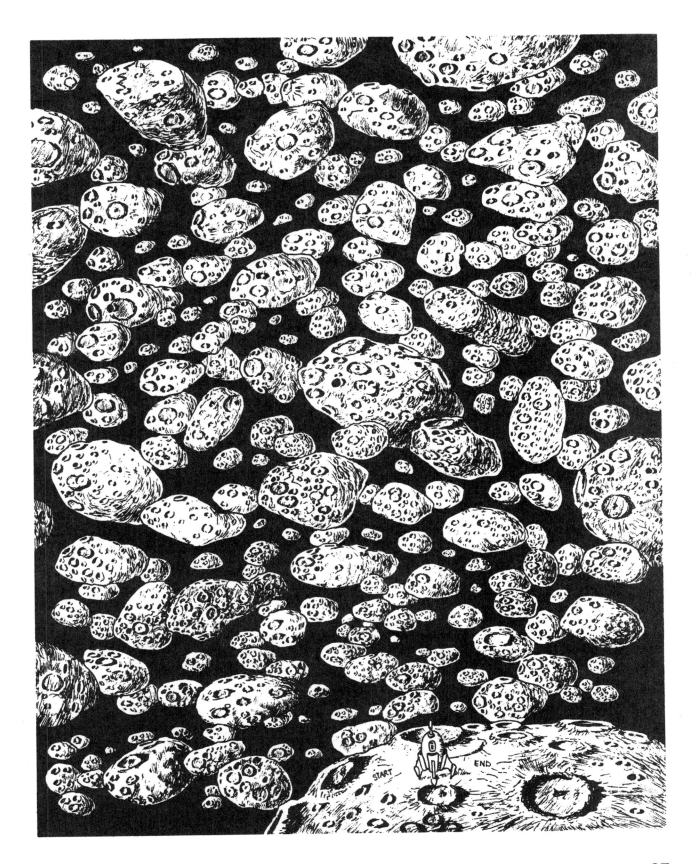

Tour of Jupiter

This planet is covered with turbulent clouds. Stay in the white clouds and find your way across Jupiter's surface.

START

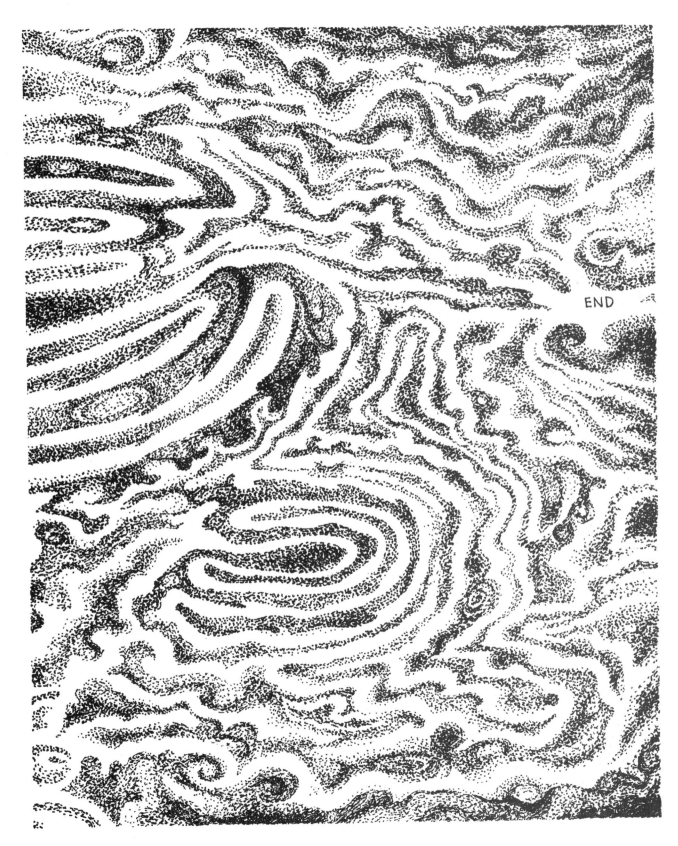

END

Tour of Saturn

Find your way around the rings of Saturn. Do not cross the dark areas.

Uranus, Neptune, and Pluto

Little is known about Uranus, Neptune, and Pluto. You will only be doing a flyby. On

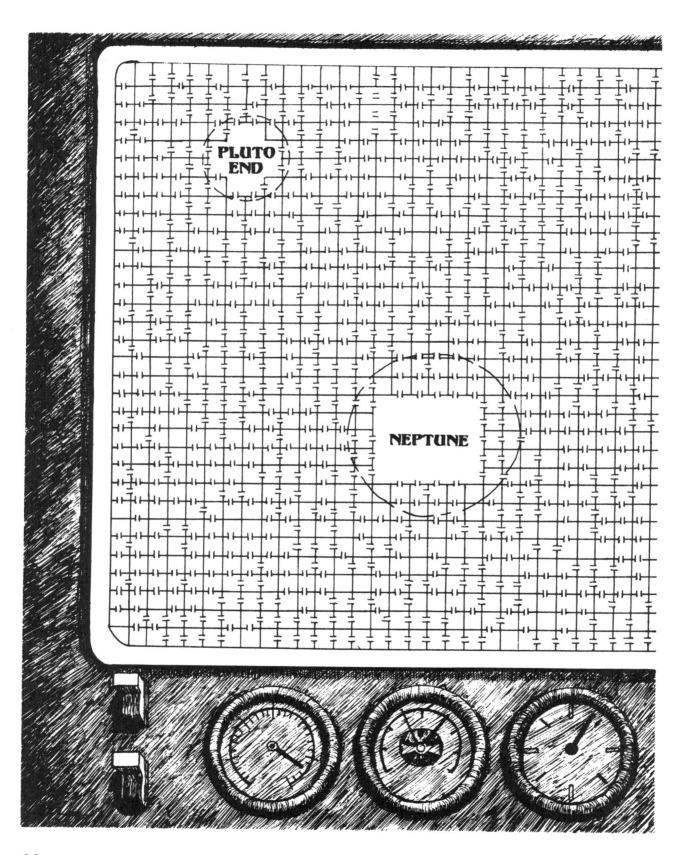

your computer screen, find a path through the openings to each planet in the order of their distance from the sun.

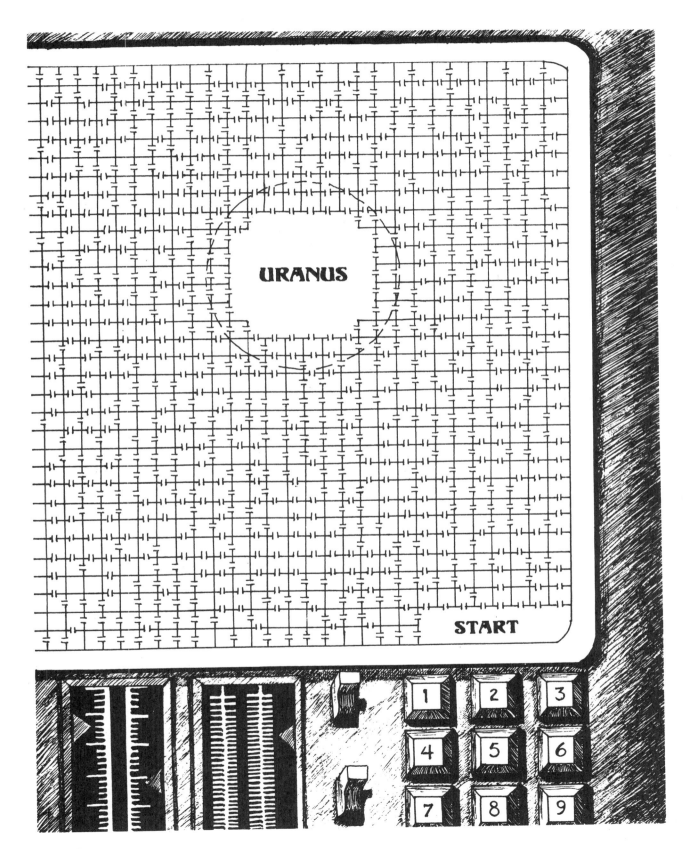

THE UNIVERSE

The size of the universe is almost beyond understanding. Distances are so great they are measured in light-years, the distance light travels in one year. Light travels 186,000 miles (300,000 kilometers) in one second. It takes light from our Sun 8 minutes to reach Earth, and 5 hours to reach Pluto. One of the closest stars to our solar system is Alpha Centauri, and it takes that star's light 4 years, 4 months to reach Earth. It is 4.3 light-years away.

There are many other interesting features in the universe, such as gas formations called nebulae, star clusters, and black holes. In addition, astronomers have recently found planets that revolve around other suns. Could they contain life? Your plan is to visit some of these features and planets.

Because of the immensity of the universe, it will be necessary for your space cruiser to reach speeds way beyond that of light for you to get home in a reasonable time. Fortunately, your spaceship is capable of such speed. So, get ready for the thrill of a lifetime.

Trip to Andromeda

Reach the Andromeda Galaxy by traveling on the connecting star beams.

Planet with Life

This planet appears to have life on it. Is it friendly life? You'd better not take any chances. Take a clear path while touring the planet and returning to the spaceship.

37

Horsehead and Orion Nebulae

Try to find a way on the space gases from the Horsehead Nebula to the Orion Nebula.

START

Exploding Star

The star you have just visited has exploded. You have only seconds to escape. Find your way on the bursting sun particles.

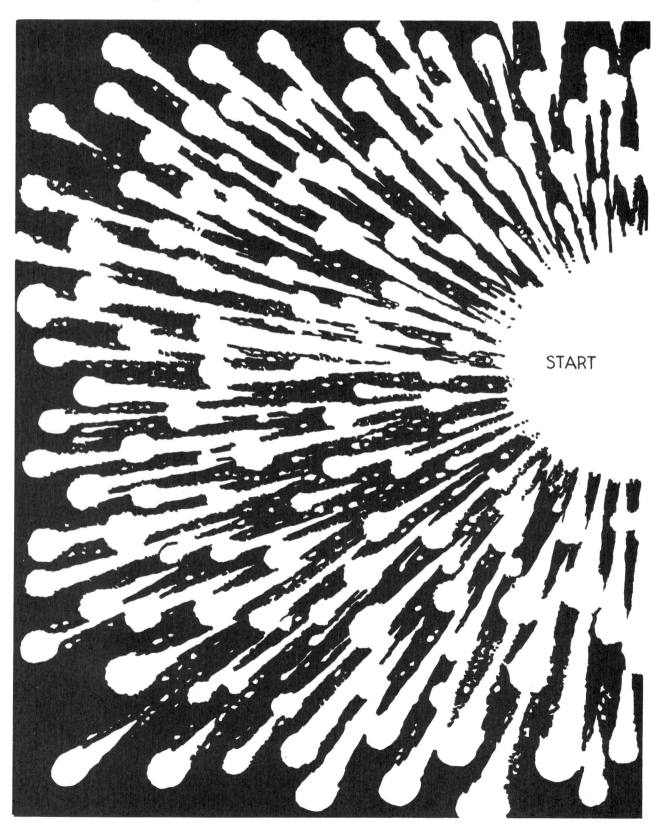

START

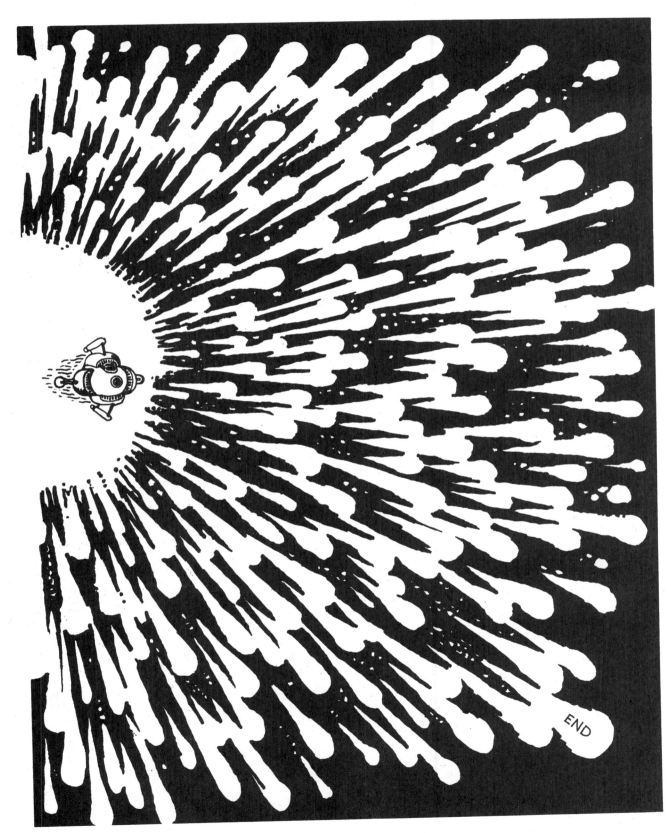

Tour of a Black Hole

The gravity from this black hole is pulling everything into it. Take a tour by finding a path on the white star matter, and be careful not to get pulled in.

Spiral Galaxies

Tour this field of spiral galaxies. You must visit the center of each galaxy only once. Stay only on the white areas, and do not backtrack.

Returning Home

Find your way home by returning to our solar system. Head back the way you came, and visit each of the features in the Universe as you return.

CONGRATULATIONS

You have been the first person to explore the solar system and universe. The information you have discovered and brought back to the scientific world is of great value. It will be studied for years to come. You have seen sights, explored worlds, and traveled distances that no one has ever accomplished before.

Also of great importance is the fact that you did not give up. You were summoned to take part in an important mission, and you met the challenge. You persevered at times when it would have been easy just to quit. For this, you will be ranked among the great astronauts.

Space Guides

If you had any trouble along the way, refer to the guides on the following pages for help.

Flight Plan Map

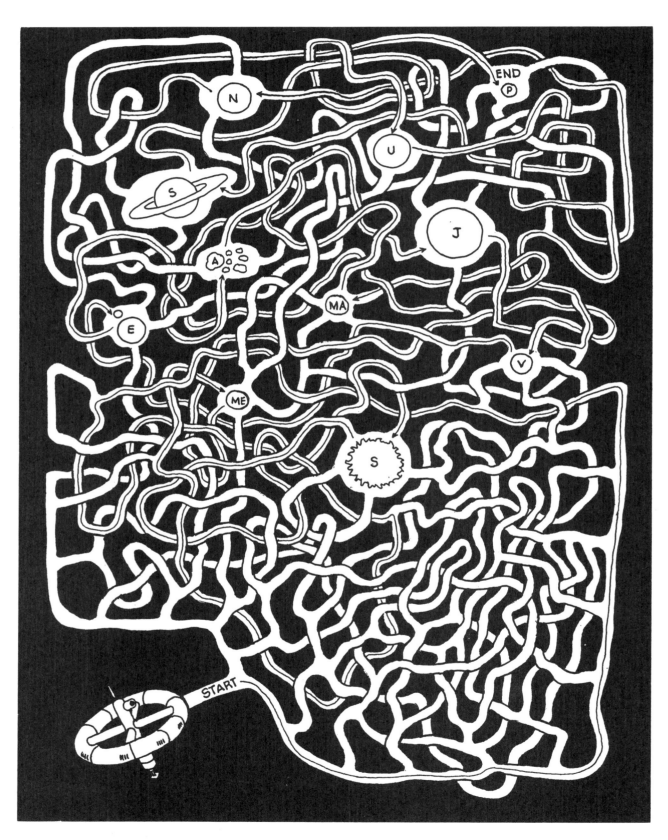

Space Shuttle

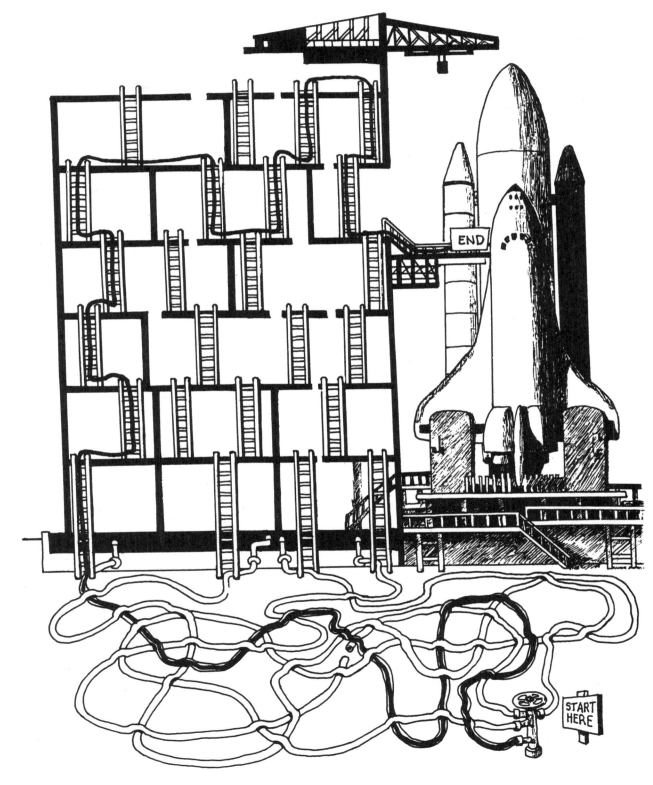

Space Station

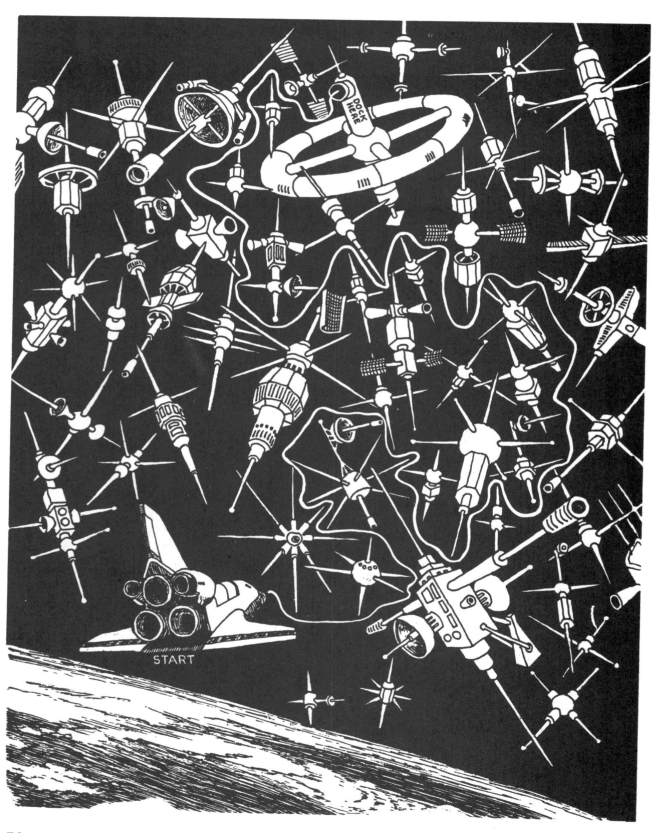

Departure

Tour of the Sun

Tour of Mercury

Tour of Venus

Tour of Earth's Moon

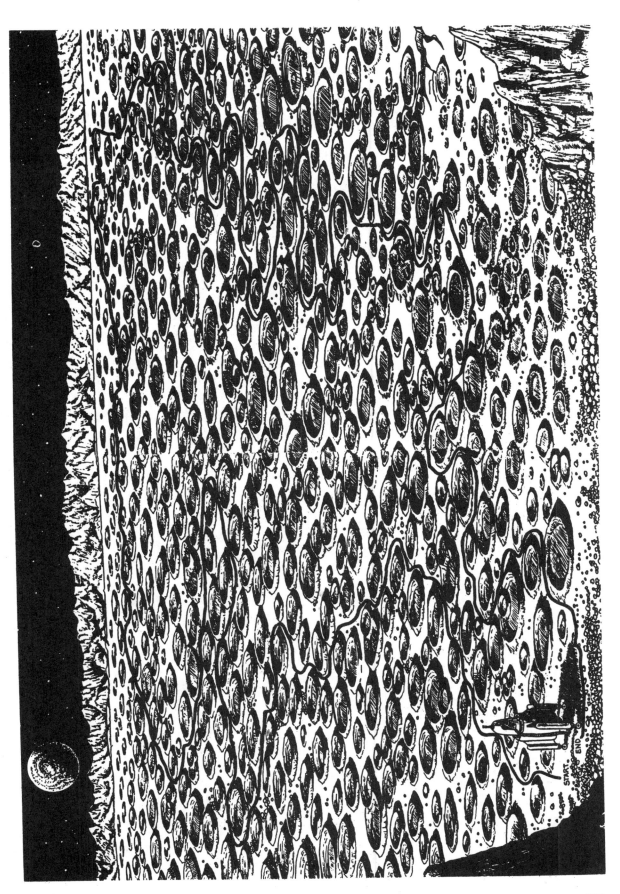

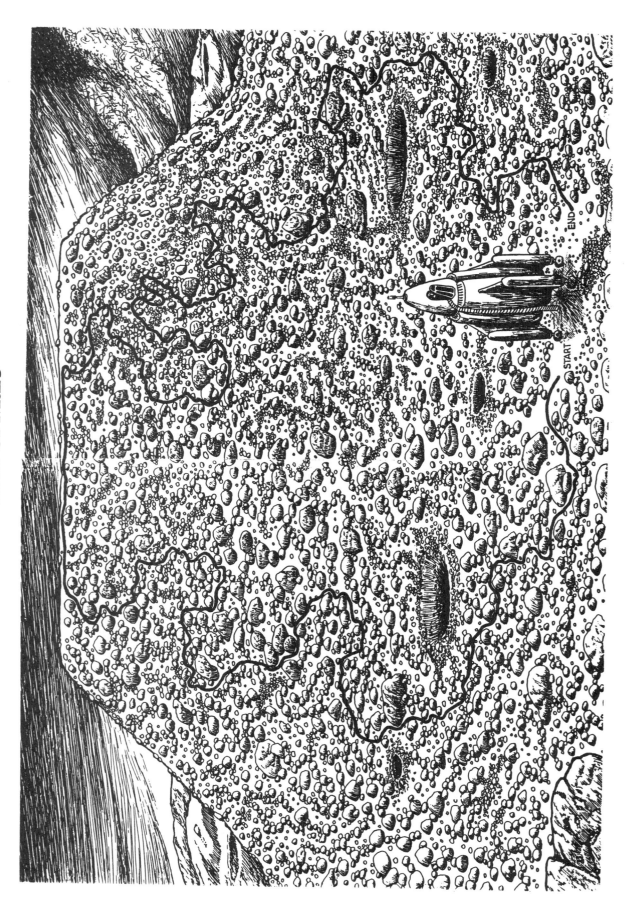

Asteroids

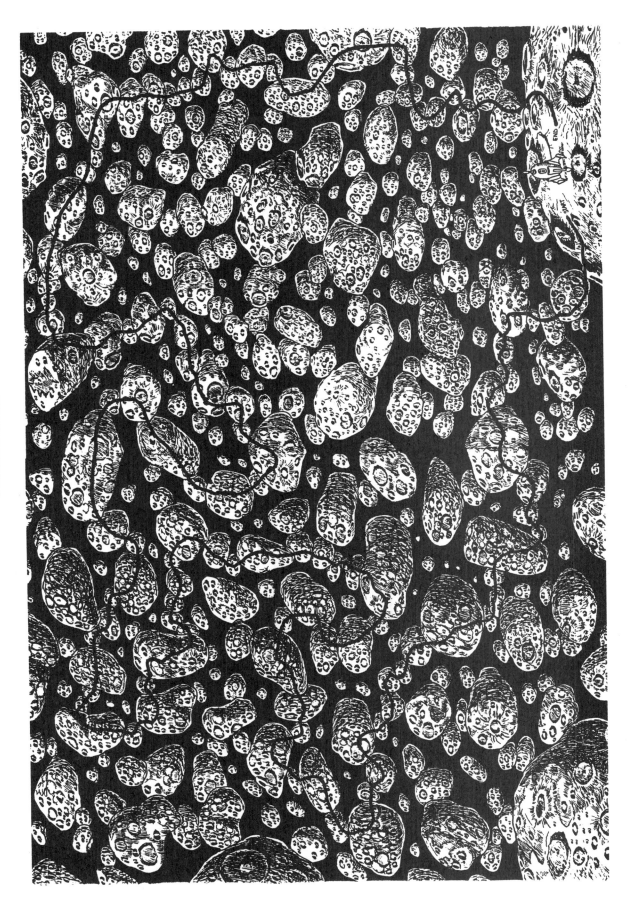

Tour of Jupiter

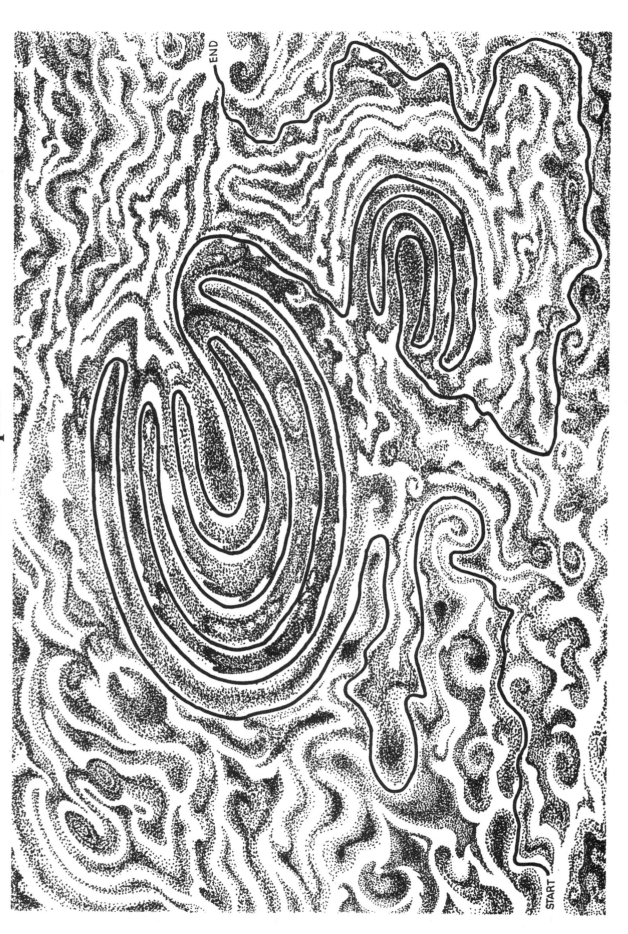

58

Tour of Saturn

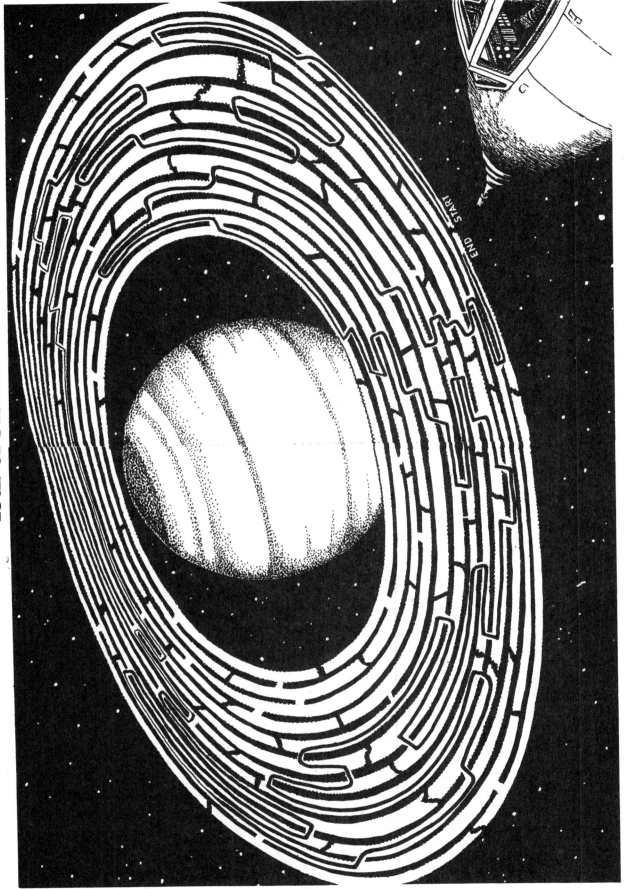

59

Uranus, Neptune, and Pluto

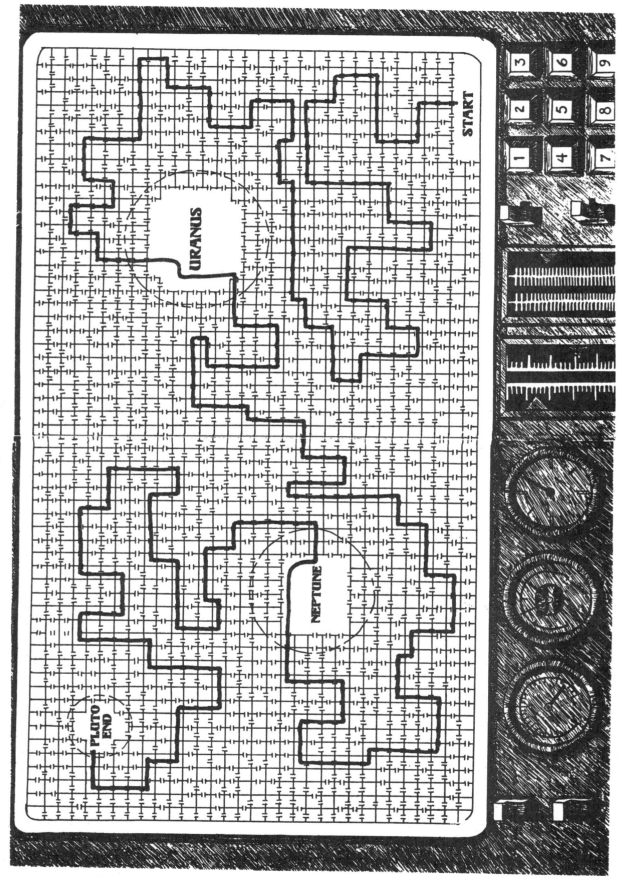

Trip to Andromeda

Planet with Life

Horsehead and Orion Nebulae

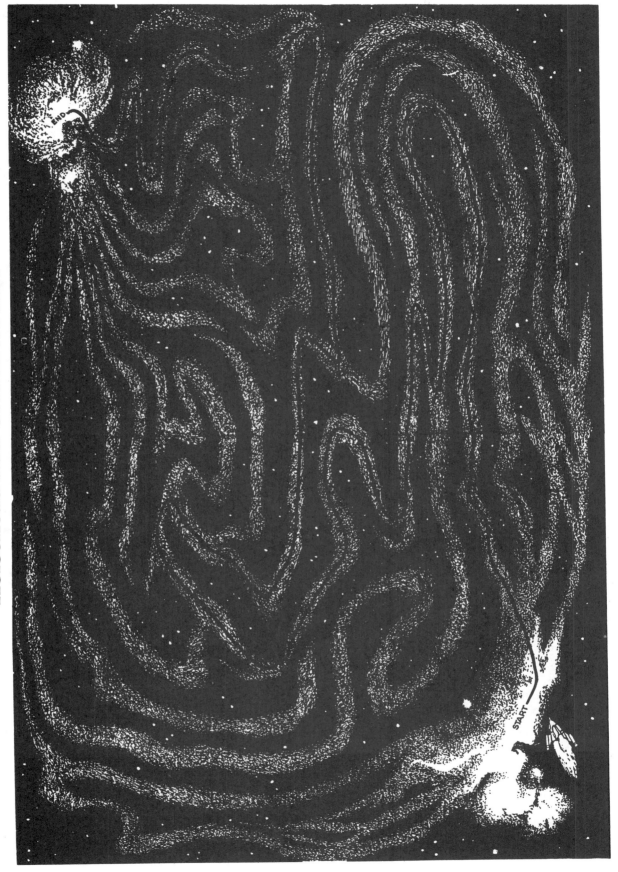

Exploding Star

Tour of a Black Hole

Spiral Galaxies

Returning Home

GREAT EXPLORER
MAZES

Roger Moreau

Contents

Introduction 73
Early Explorers 74
Great Wall of China 75
San Salvador Island 76
India Spice Shop 78
Indian Cliff Dwellings 79
Inside an Indian Cliff Dwelling 80
Hudson Bay 82
Cape Horn 83

19th-Century Explorers 84
Kent Peninsula 85
Missouri River 86
Lake Victoria 88
Gulf of Carpentaria 90

20th-Century Explorers 92
North Pole 93
South Pole 95
Machu Picchu 97
Tomb of Tutankhamen 99
Tranquillity Base 102
Titanic 104
French Cave 106

Congratulations 108
Explorer's Guides 108

INTRODUCTION

The urge to explore and discover began with the very first people. These explorers probably went forth when they began to wonder what was on the other side of the hill, beyond the mountain range, or around the river bend. This urge has taken man from ocean to ocean, continent to continent, and now into space. It is a fascinating and exciting story that began long ago, goes on today, and will continue.

What is known as the Great Age of Discovery began in the 1400s, when countries in Europe desired to make money by trading with the Indies. When the Turks blocked popular Eastern trade routes after 1453, Europeans set out to find new routes. They had newer, faster, and more seaworthy ships that could hold greater loads than earlier ships, so, over the next 200 years, they sailed on the oceans, discovering and exploring new lands and finding new routes. During that time they found out more about the world than had ever been known before.

Many explorers were away from home for years. They suffered greatly and sometimes gave their lives. Their efforts required uncommon courage, strength, determination, and perseverance. They sometimes experienced the joy of victory, and too often suffered great defeat. The successful explorers had to be men of unselfish character who had complete dedication to their quests.

On the following pages you will have a chance to learn about many great explorers and follow in their footsteps. The way will not be easy. It will take courage, determination, and perseverance on your part to be successful. Even though you will face danger, sacrificing your life will, fortunately, never be required.

Now, boldly go forth . . . as they did. Good luck!

Roger Moreau

EARLY EXPLORERS

Marco Polo was an Italian explorer who explored central Asia and China between 1271 and 1292. He helped bring unknown information about the Orient back to Europe. He also made friends with the famous Mongol conqueror Kublai Khan, who gave Polo many gifts. Now, you have to reach Kublai Khan's camp **(page 75).** Find a clear path. You can go up and down ladders and through tower openings when you travel on the Great Wall of China.

Christopher Columbus set sail from Spain on August 3, 1492, hoping to find a new route to the East by sailing west. His fleet consisted of three ships: the *Santa María*, the *Pinta*, and the *Niña*. They were sailing into unknown waters, and the three ships were greatly affected by the wind and currents. Finally, on October 12, 1492, Columbus sighted land, an island he named San Salvador. Now, *you* have to stay within the wind and current lines as you retrace Columbus's route **(pages 76 and 77).** You must visit every island, and you cannot sail back over your own route.

The Portuguese explorer *Vasco da Gama* because the first person to sail around the Cape of Good Hope to India, in May 1498. When he returned with a cargo of spice, the king promoted him to the rank of Admiral of the Sea of India. See if you can bring back spices from India like da Gama **(page 78).** There are many dangers. Find a clear path. If you're successful, maybe you'll also get a promotion.

Francisco Vásquez de Coronado was a Spaniard who explored the American Southwest in 1540. He was in search of the Seven Cities of Cibola and hoped to find gold. Instead, he discovered many ancient Indian dwellings, the Continental Divide, and the Grand Canyon. In this maze **(page 79),** climb the ladders to reach the cliff dwellings.

When Coronado entered this dwelling **(pages 80 and 81),** he was sure he'd find gold. You were probably expecting to, also. Sorry! Be careful not to disturb the tarantulas as you find a clear and fast exit to the right.

Henry Hudson was a British sea captain who hoped to find a passage to the Far East by sailing around North America. He explored the northeast coast of America and on his fourth voyage, in 1610, entered Hudson Bay. In this maze **(page 82),** you have to try to find a way, by ship, to get to Hudson Bay. Use this map. It was drawn by one of Hudson's sailors who, unfortunately, was seasick when he drew it.

James Cook was a British mariner, who made many voyages exploring and mapping the regions in the South Pacific Ocean. On his first voyage there in 1768, he sailed around Cape Horn and reached New Zealand, where he mapped the North and South Islands. Rounding Cape Horn is no simple task, as you will see **(page 83).** The winds are harsh and the waves high. Find your way between the waves to reach the Pacific.

Great Wall of China

To reach Kublai Khan's camp, navigate a clear path on and around the Great Wall of China. You can go up and down ladders and through tower openings.

San Salvador Island

To retrace Christopher Columbus's route to San Salvador Island, make sure you stay

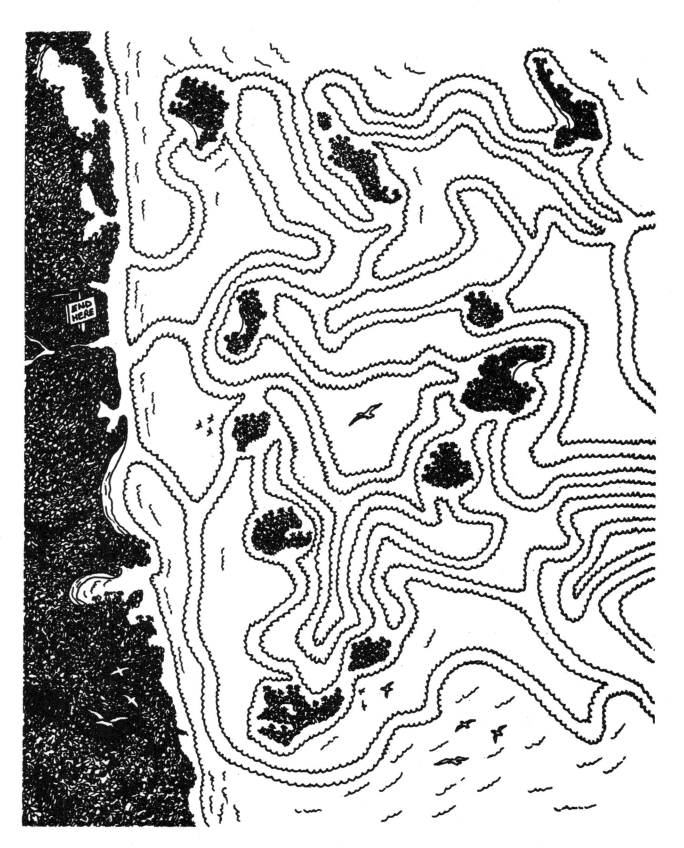

END HERE

within the wind and current lines, that you visit every island, and that you do not sail back over your own route.

India Spice Shop

To reach the Spice Shop of India, you must find a clear path past the animals and other hazards and over the openings in the earth.

Indian Cliff Dwellings

To reach the ancient Indian cliff dwellings, climb the ladders.

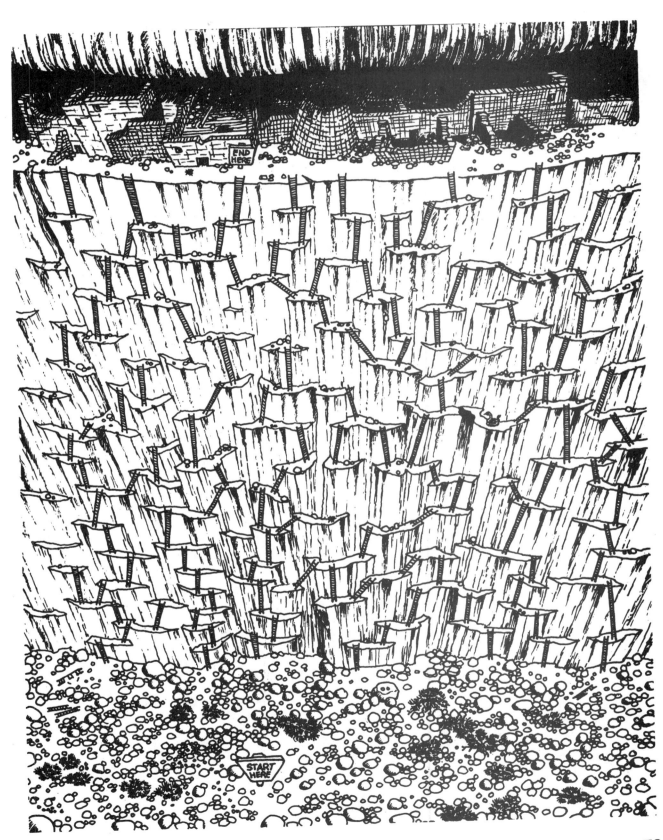

Inside an Indian Cliff Dwelling

There is no gold in this cliff dwelling, only tarantulas. To reach the exit, find a path through them.

Hudson Bay

To sail to Hudson Bay, find the right tributary.

Cape Horn

To round Cape Horn and reach the Pacific Ocean, you must find your way between the waves.

19TH-CENTURY EXPLORERS

For many years, starting as early as the 1500s, explorers attempted unsuccessfully to find a Northwest Passage. *John Franklin* was a British naval explorer who made three attempts in the early 1800s. On his third expedition, in 1821, while Franklin was attempting to map the Arctic coastline, tragedy struck. An early winter set in and all of the expedition perished. In this maze **(page 85)**, you must find your way up the Hood River to Coronation Gulf, which is choked with blocks of ice. Find your way through the ice to reach Kent Peninsula. A herd of caribou is passing through the area, so avoid the places on the river where they block the way. Try to get through before winter sets in.

In May 1804, *Meriwether Lewis* and *William Clark* set out to travel up the Missouri River in an effort to find and map a way to the Pacific Ocean. Their journey took two years and covered 8,000 miles round-trip. Finding their way wasn't easy. They got help from an Indian woman named Sacagawea, who served as a guide and interpreter during their westward march in Shoshone Indian country. On **pages 86 and 87**, you must find your way up the Missouri River, and then up eastward-flowing streams to the Continental Divide—the area that extends south-southeast from northwest Canada to South America. Next, find the right trail that will enable you to discover a westward-flowing stream that will take you to the mighty Columbia River and the Pacific Ocean. You won't have Sacagawea to help you, but you will have an old Indian map.

During the mid-19th century, a great effort was made in Africa to find the headwaters of the Nile River. In 1858, two British explorers, *Richard Burton* and *John Hanning Speke*, discovered Lake Victoria and suggested that it might be the source of the White Nile. In 1866, *David Livingstone*, a Scottish medical missionary, set out to find the source of the White Nile and was not heard from for several years. In 1869, a British reporter named *Henry Stanley* set out to find Livingstone. He found him at Lake Tanganyika, which had been discovered by Burton and Speke in 1858. When he first saw Livingstone, he uttered those famous words, "Dr. Livingstone, I presume?" See if you can find your way up the White Nile to Lake Victoria **(pages 88 and 89)**. You must row upstream to the falls and then hike around any falls to get into the streams above them. You can go up and down the streams, but you cannot row up any falls.

In 1860–1861, the Irishman *Robert O'Hara Burke* and his English companion, *William Wills*, became the first men to cross Australia from south to north. On the return trek, they died of starvation. Follow their route from Melbourne to the Gulf of Carpentaria **(pages 90 and 91)**. Find a clear path and take plenty of food and water.

Kent Peninsula

To find your way through the ice to reach Kent Peninsula, make sure you use a path that is not blocked by caribou.

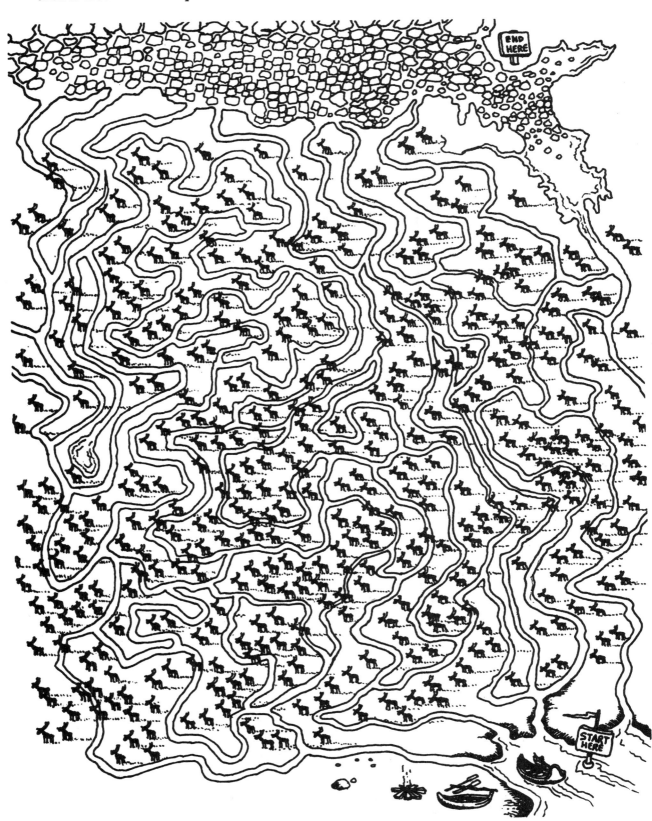

Missouri River

Your goal here is to find the correct path up the Missouri River to the Continental

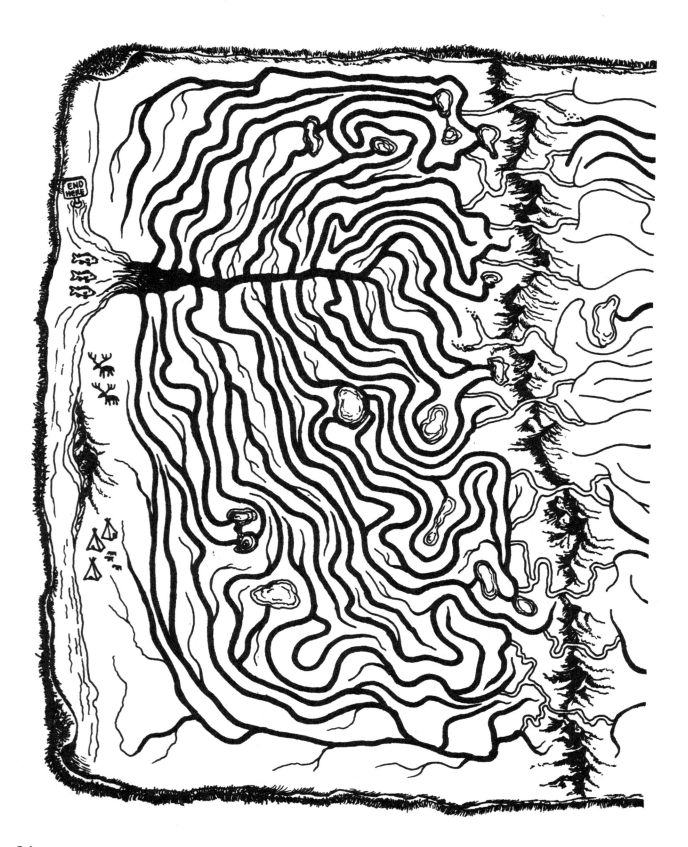

Divide, and then the trail that will take you from the Continental Divide to the Columbia River to the Pacific Ocean.

Lake Victoria

To get to Lake Victoria from the Nile River, find the correct stream to the falls, and the

correct path from the falls to the lake. Remember, you can move up and down the streams, but you cannot row up the falls.

Gulf of Carpentaria

To navigate the route from Melbourne to the Gulf of Carpentaria, find a path that avoids the wildlife and other hazards and crosses the openings in the earth.

20TH-CENTURY EXPLORERS

Commander Robert E. Peary was an American explorer who was the first man to reach the North Pole, on April 6, 1909. He trekked over drifting pack ice for 413 nautical miles. Now, you have to get to the North Pole **(page 93)**. The ice is always cracking and moving. Avoid the cracks in the pack ice and keep dry. Now that you're there you must return **(page 94)**—a trip of 413 nautical miles. Note that the ice has changed. Good luck!

After Peary reached the North Pole, the race was on for the South Pole. Two explorers, *Roald Amundsen* of Norway and *Robert Falcon Scott* of Great Britain, were involved in the race between 1910 and 1912. Each went by a different route. The distance to the South Pole was about 900 miles. Amundsen reached the Pole first, on December 14, 1911. He left his tent there, which Scott found when he arrived a few months later. On the return trip, Scott and his four companions froze to death. Now, you must find a path to the Pole **(page 95)**.

You made it! Now, you must get back—a trip of 900 miles **(page 96)**. Is it possible?

Hiram Bingham was an American explorer who discovered Machu Picchu, an ancient Inca city 6,270 feet high in the Andes, in 1911. Follow his map to the ancient city **(page 97)**. You can go under and on the overpasses.

Now, climb the steep trail to the city **(page 98)**. It could be tough.

Howard Carter was an English archaeologist who discovered the undisturbed tomb of the pharaoh Tutankhamen in 1922. The opening was a stairway found under tons of rocks in the Valley of the Kings in Egypt. Find a clear path to the stairway **(page 99)**. Now, explore the tomb and find King Tut **(p. 100 and 101)**. Avoid the debris and snakes.

On July 20–21, 1969, the crew of Apollo 11—*Neil Armstrong, Edwin Aldrin, Jr.* and *Michael Collins*—broadcast to earth from the moon, "Houston, Tranquillity Base here. The 'Eagle' has landed." Then, as Neil Armstrong stepped from the lunar module footpad onto the moon, he announced, "That's one small step for a man, one giant leap for mankind." Man had finally set foot on the moon. Now, you have a chance to explore Tranquillity Base **(pages 102 and 103)**. Do not step on or over any rocks or into any shadows.

In April 1912, the luxury ship *Titanic* struck an iceberg in the North Atlantic and went down with a loss of 1,522 people. On September 1, 1985, Robert Ballard found the *Titanic* 13,000 feet down on the ocean floor. See if you can find it in the maze **(page 104)**. A grid has been placed over the search area. Move through the openings to try to find the *Titanic*.

Explore the *Titanic* **(page 105)**. Find a clear path over the top surface of the ship.

In France, caves have been found with beautiful ancient paintings covering the walls. Now, you can discover one **(pages 106 and 107)**. This is your chance to be included with the great explorers of the past. If you are successful at exploring your discovery, name the cave after yourself. But, remember, once you go in you have to be able to get out.

North Pole

To follow in the footsteps of Commander Robert Peary and reach the North Pole, find the correct path that avoids the cracks in the ice.

North Pole

Now that you've reached the North Pole, you must find your way back.

South Pole

Now, try your luck at finding the South Pole. Once again, avoid the cracks in the ice.

South Pole

Now that you have reached the South Pole, you must find your way back.

Machu Picchu

To travel to the ancient Inca city of Machu Picchu, you have to go under and on the overpasses.

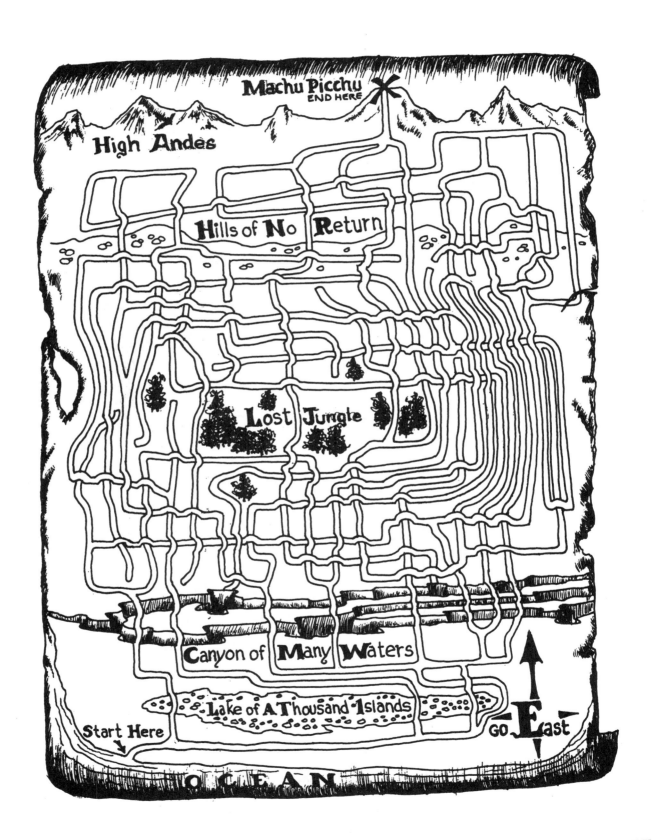

Machu Picchu

Now, climb the steep trail to the city.

Tomb of Tutankhamen

Find a path to the stairway that leads to the tomb of Tutankhamen.

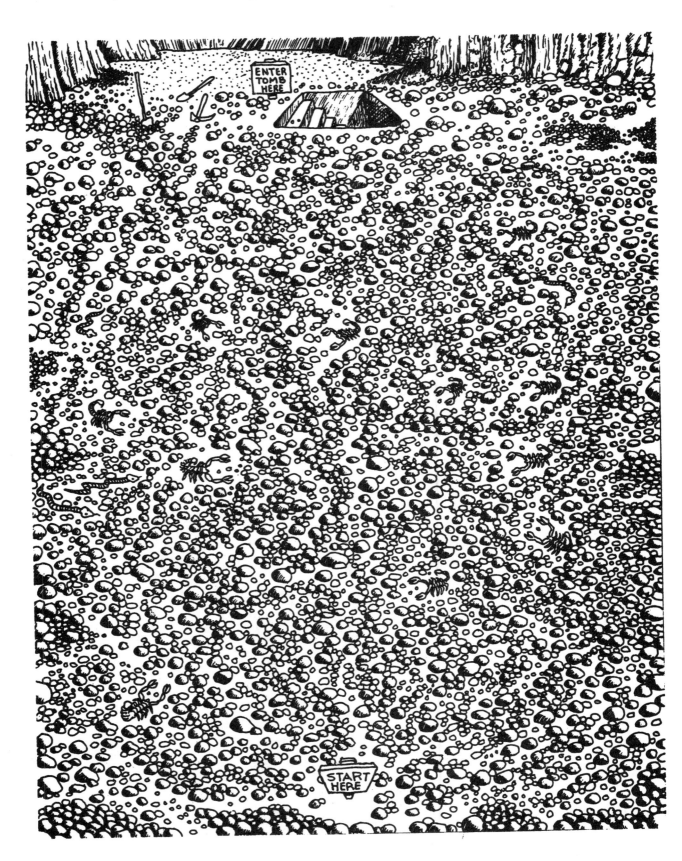

Tomb of Tutankhamen

Now that you're inside the tomb, find a path past the debris and snakes to find King Tut.

Tranquillity Base

Now that you've landed on the Moon, find a path around Tranquillity Base. Do not step on or over any rocks or into any shadows.

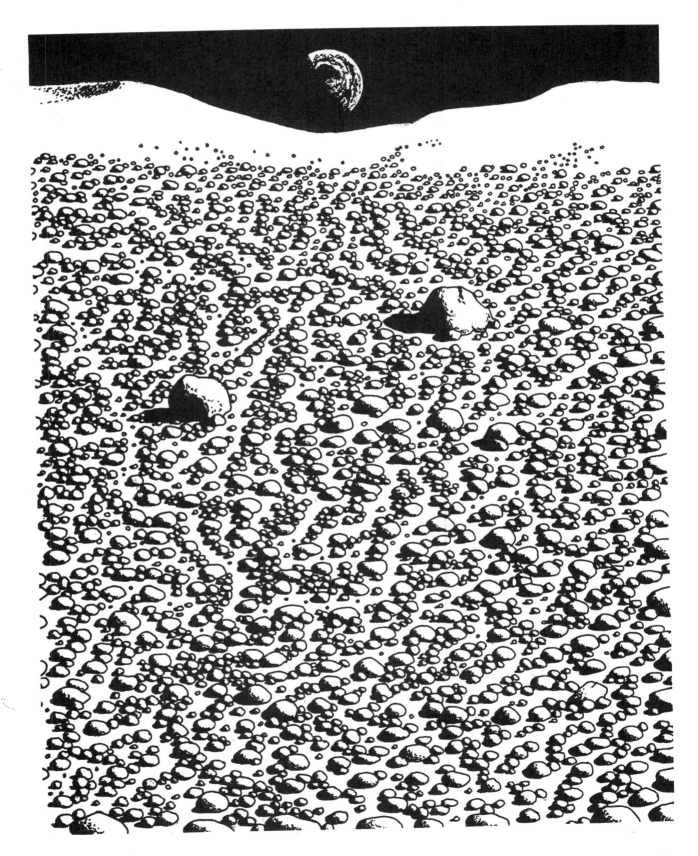

Titanic

To reach the *Titanic,* maneuver through the openings in the maze.

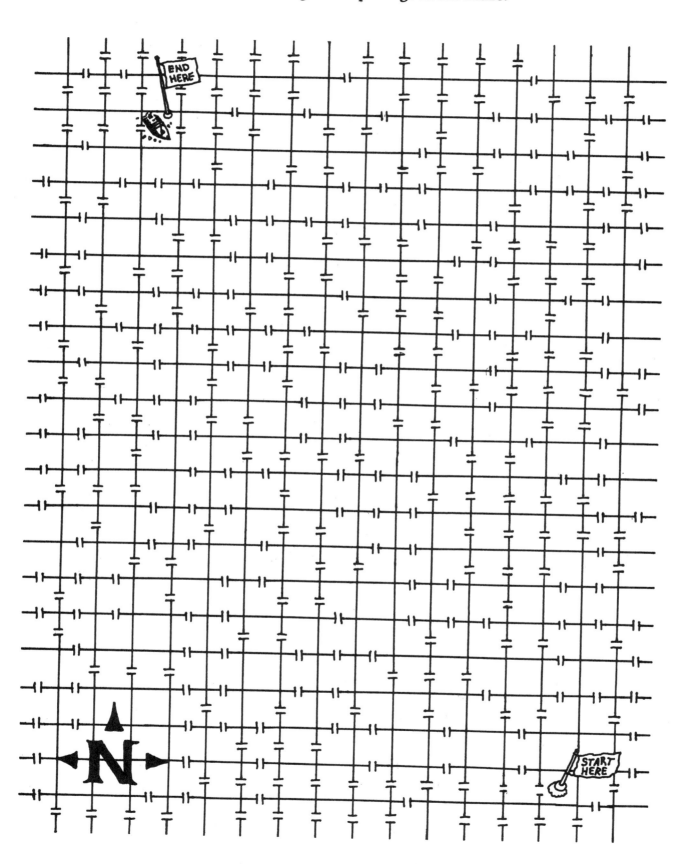

Titanic

Now that you've found the *Titanic*, explore it by traveling along a path on the top surface of the ship.

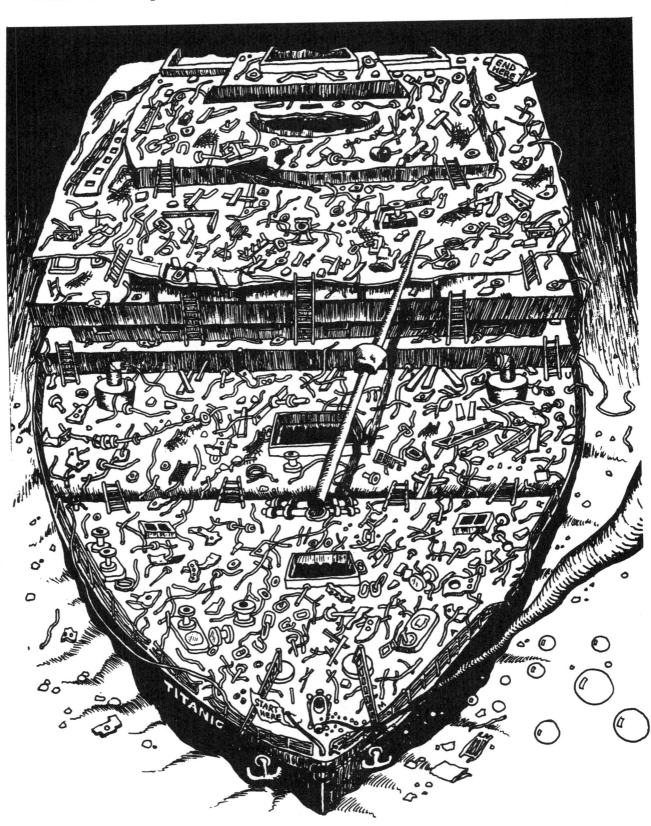

French Cave

Chart a path through this cave in the hopes of discovering ancient paintings.

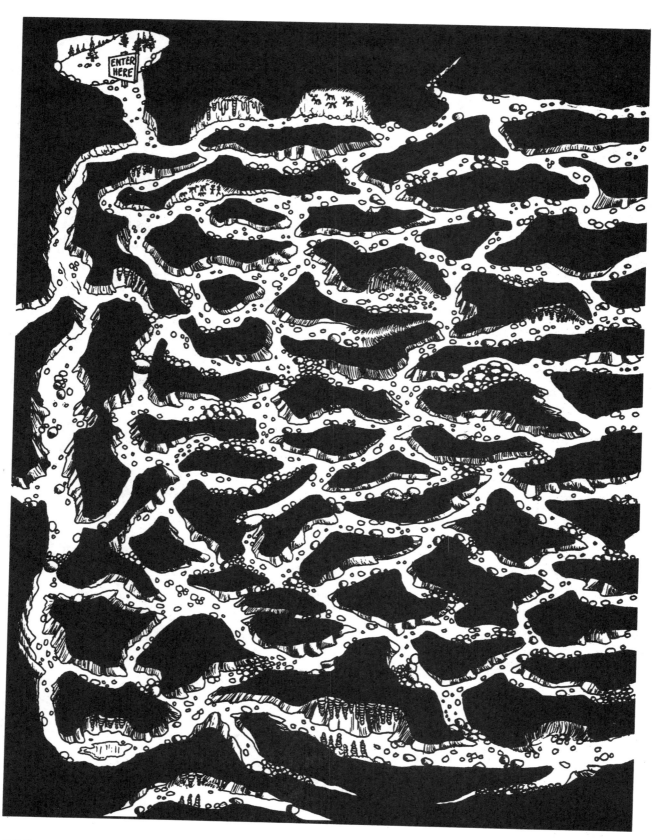

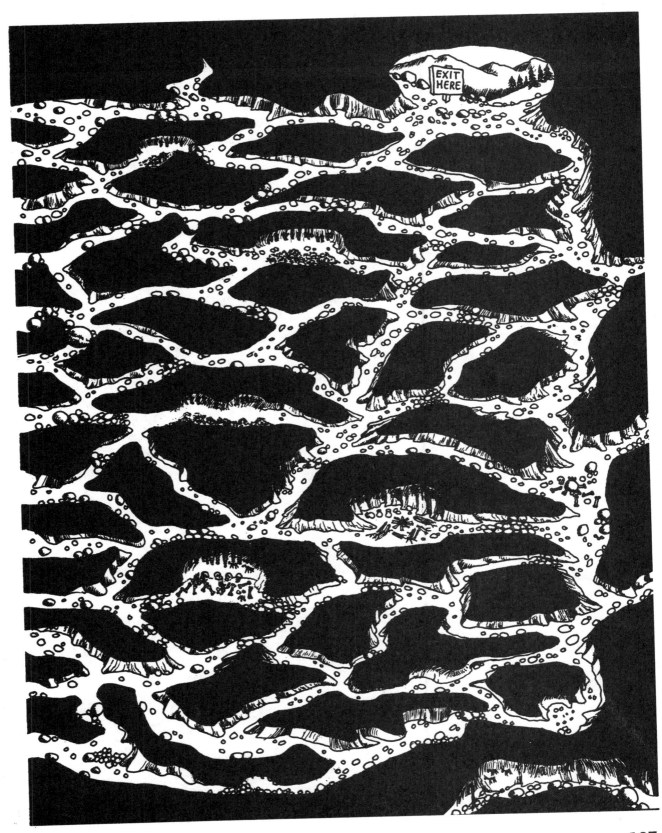

CONGRATULATIONS!

You have been successful in following in the footsteps of many of the great explorers of the past, and have learned how important it is not to get discouraged or give up. There is an exciting world out there for you to explore. Now, go forth with all the courage and determination of those past explorers and make your mark in whatever you choose to do. Remember, strive to know what is over the hill, beyond the mountain range, and around the bend in the river.

EXPLORER'S GUIDES

If you had any trouble finding your way through the mazes in this book, use the explorer's guides on the following pages. These guides should be used only in case of an emergency. The guide shown below is for the cover maze.

Great Wall of China

San Salvador Island

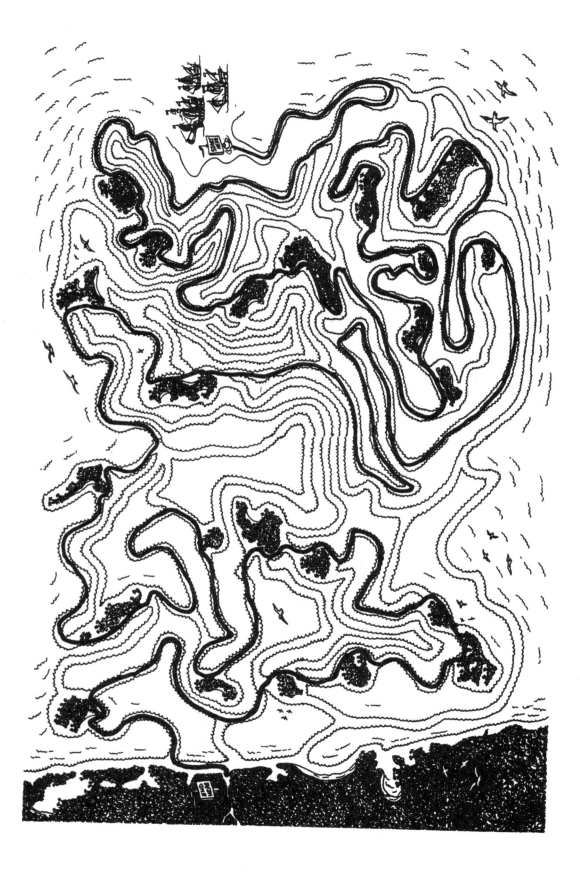

India Spice Shop

Indian Cliff Dwellings

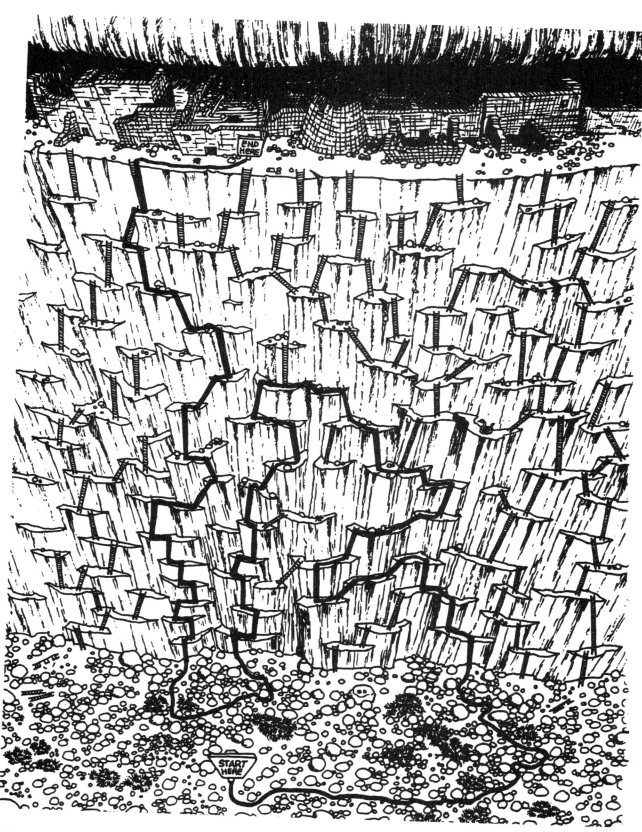

Inside an Indian Cliff Dwelling

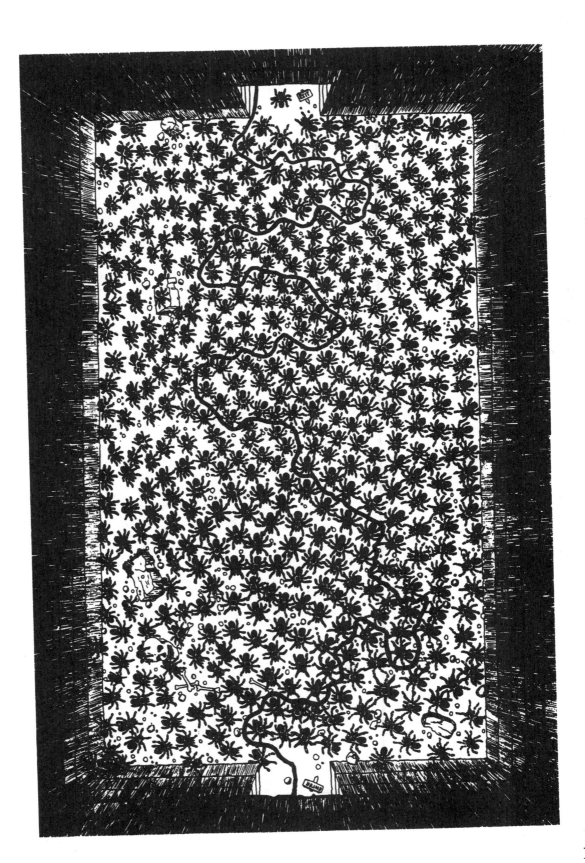

Hudson Bay

Cape Horn

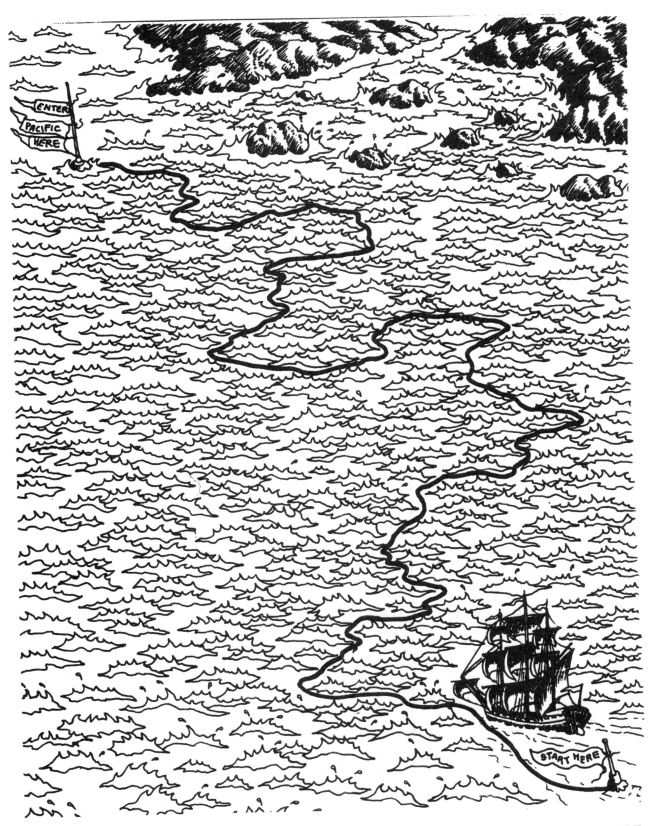

Kent Peninsula

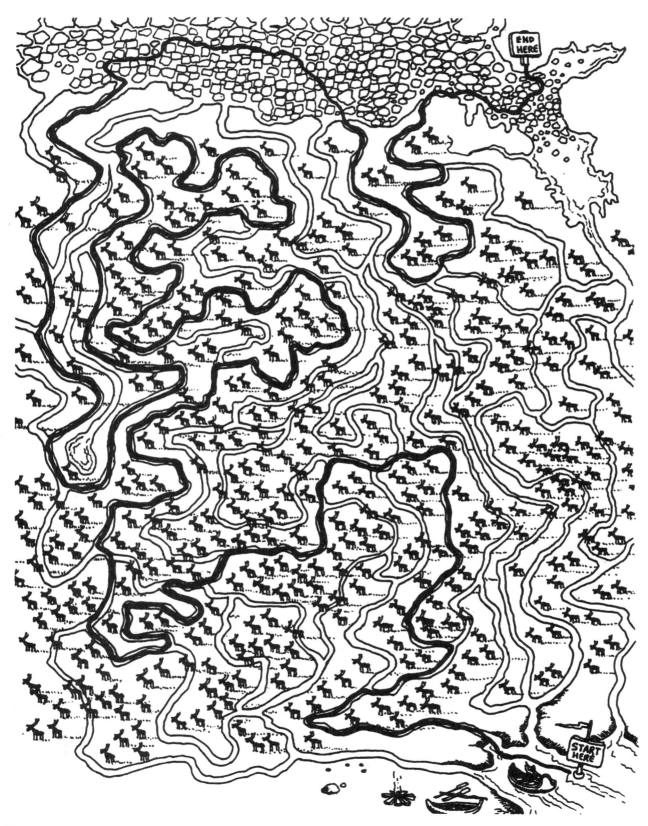

Missouri River

Lake Victoria

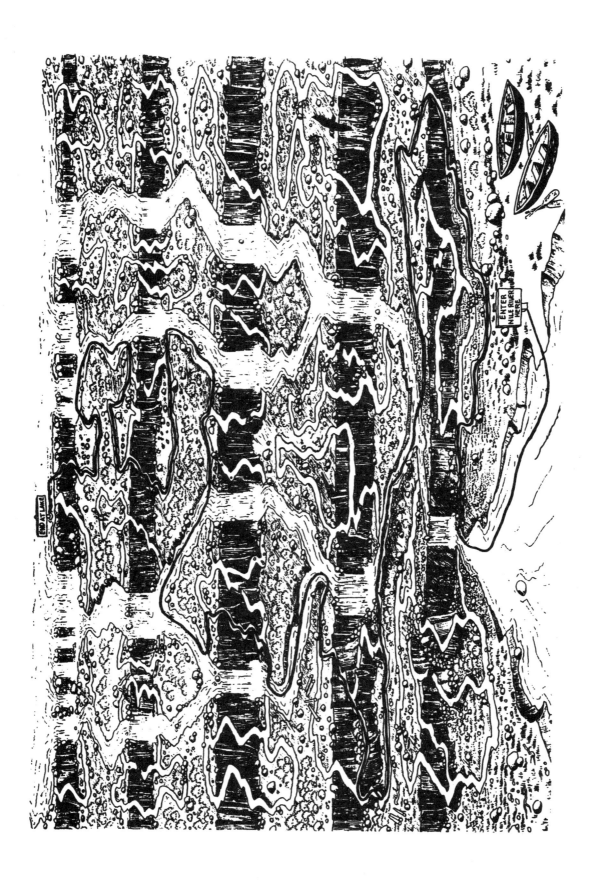

Gulf of Carpentaria

North Pole

North Pole

South Pole

South Pole

Machu Picchu

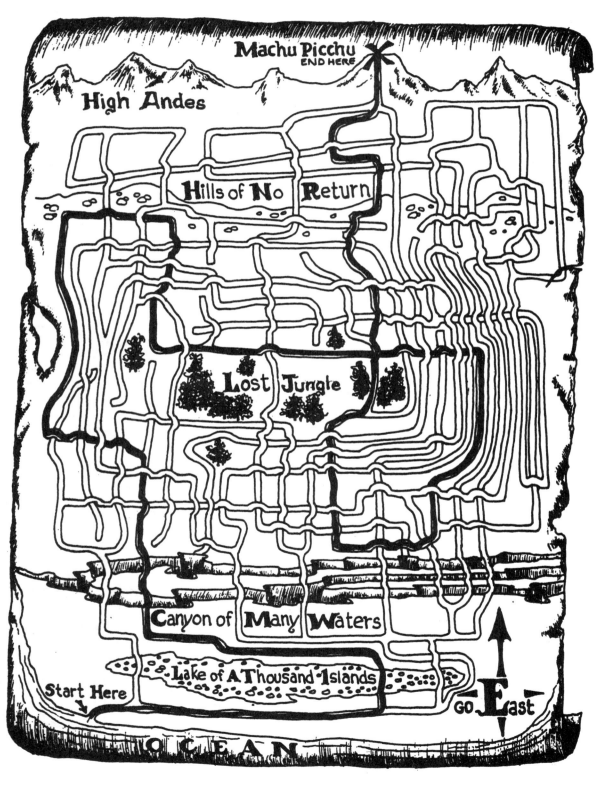

Machu Picchu

Tomb of Tutankhamen

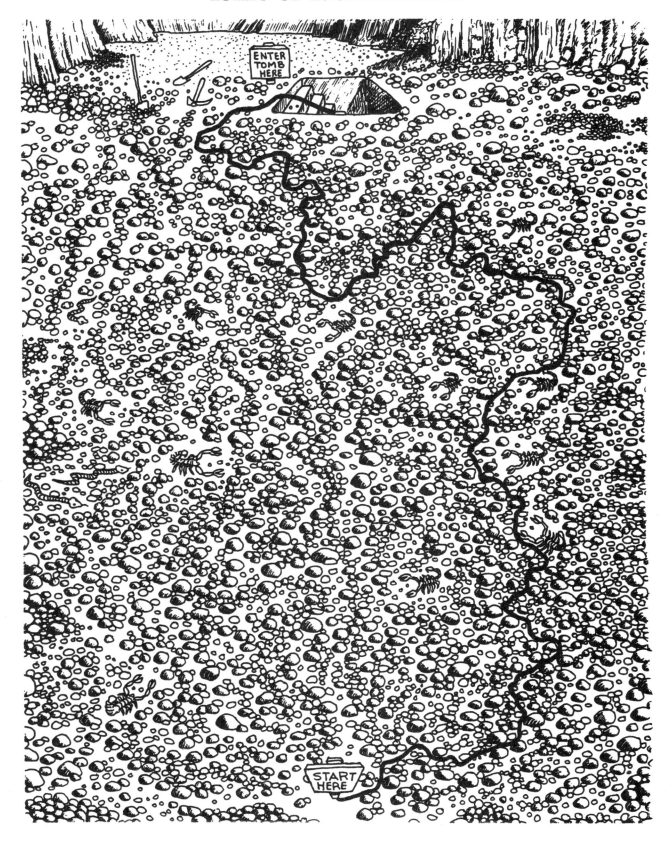

Tomb of Tutankhamen

Tranquility Base

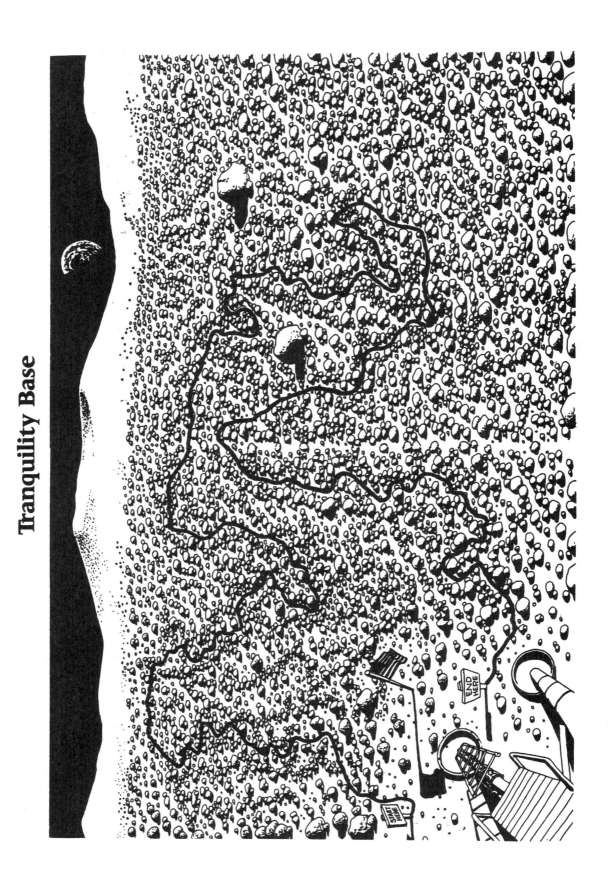

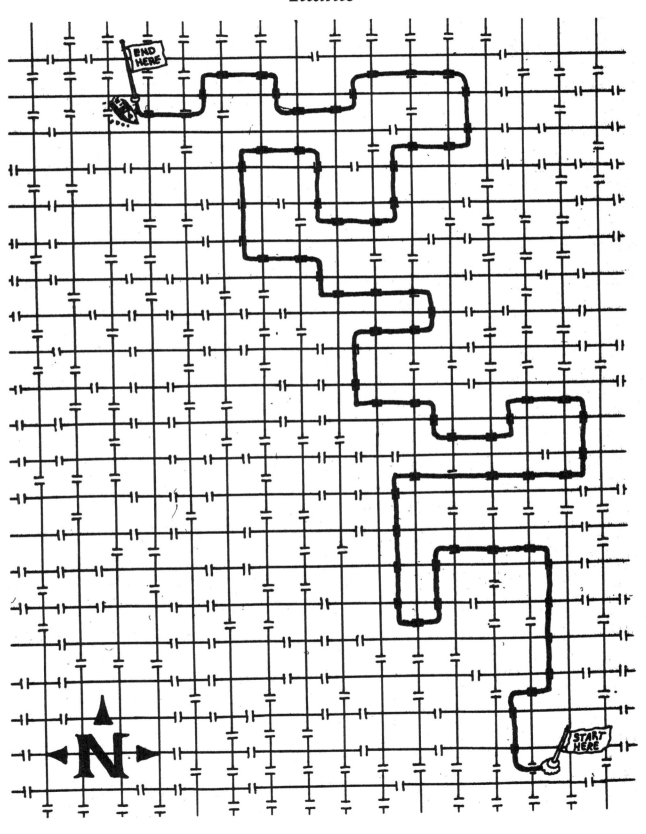

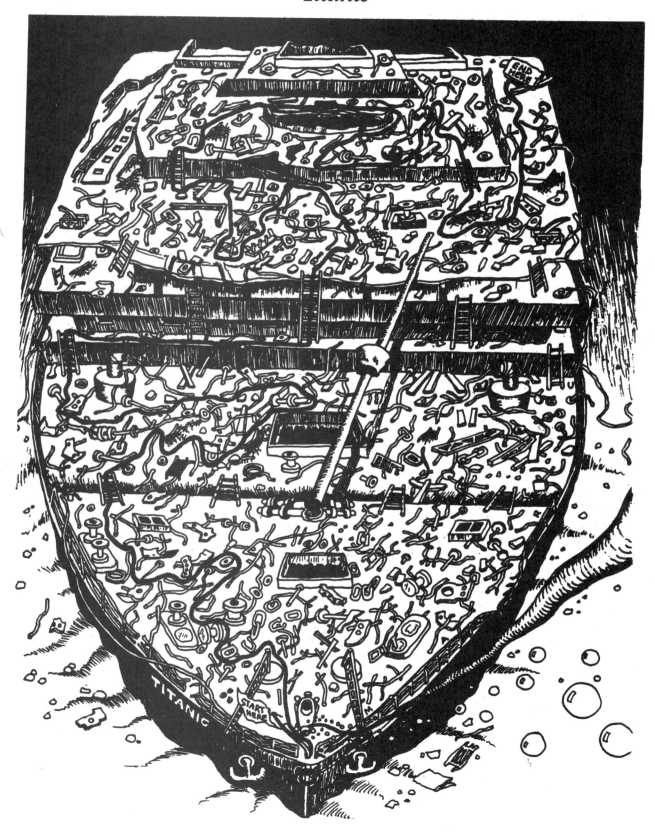

French Cave

SAVE THE EARTH
MAZE BOOK

Contents

Introduction 136
Oceans & Streams 137
Save the Dolphin 138
Free the Fishes 139
Help the Salmon 140
Free the Whale 142
Prevent Atomic Testing 144
Help the Turtle 146

Wildlife 147
Help the Duck Family 148
Waterponds for Waterfowl 150
Save the Spotted Owl 152
Feed the Baby Eagles 153
Save the Elephants and Rhinos 154
Arrest the Poacher 156
Save the Rain Forest 158
Save the Panda 160
Save the California Condor 162

Pollution 163
Fight the Oil Spill 164
Stop Acid Rain 165
Stop Nuclear Waste Dumping 166
Clean Up the Park 167
Stop Lake Pollution 168
Produce Fresh Drinking Water 170
Stop Air Pollution 171

Congratulations 173
Help for Earth Savers 173

Introduction

The great planet Earth we live on has in the past been called many names that have described its condition. They were friendly, healthy names like the "Good Earth" and "Mother Earth." We could take comfort in knowing that Earth could sustain us and provide for us. In recent times, however, our planet has taken on a new name, a name which is both depressing and frightening. It describes an Earth that is in grave danger, an Earth that may no longer be able to provide for or sustain us. The Earth of today is called the "Endangered Earth."

The Earth is in danger because of the negligence and carelessness of man. Such problems as air pollution, acid rain, water pollution, toxic waste, species extinction, fisheries depletion, deforestation, and radiation peril are just a few of the man-made problems. If something isn't done soon to end the mistreatment, it will be too late to save planet Earth.

On the following pages, you will learn about some of these problems; but of more importance, you will have a chance to do something about it. If you are successful, you could help in taking a great step toward saving Earth!

For practice start with the cover, where smoke from a careless fire is covering the sky. Carry the water through the jungle and up the mountain to put out the fire.

It will not be easy. Nothing worth having comes easily. So don't give up. Face each problem with courage and determination and when you succeed Mother Earth will thank you.

Oceans and Streams

Water pollution from acid rain, fertilizers, and urban runoff has affected our oceans and streams. Combined with overfishing and our altering of the natural flow of rivers, these man-made problems endanger wildlife and threaten the ecological balance. The mazes on the next few pages present some of these problems.

SAVE THE DOLPHIN

A dolphin is entangled in some rotting gill nets. You can save it by finding a clear pathway through the rotting nets and untangling it.

FREE THE FISHES

In this overfished area several fish are hooked and snagged on the bottom. They will die if you don't find a clear path down to them between the lines and hooks.

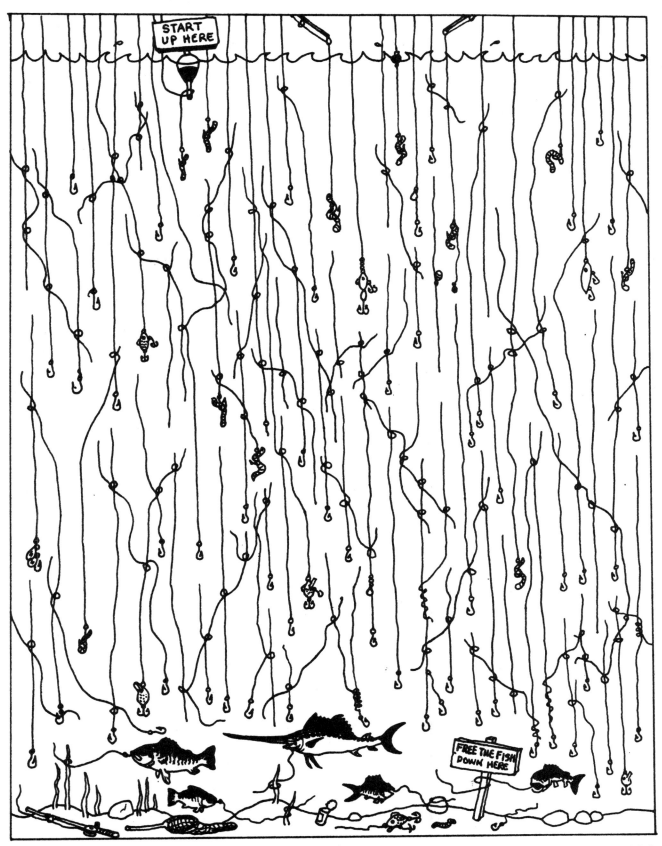

HELP THE SALMON

The river has been dammed many times. The dams confuse the salmon that want to

START HERE

return to where they were born to lay their eggs. Help them find a way around the dams to reach the stream.

END HERE

BAIT

FREE THE WHALE

This whale lost its way while migrating south. It turned into San Francisco Bay and

swam up the creeks that flow through the marshes at the back of the bay. Help him find his way back to the ocean.

PREVENT ATOMIC TESTING

This island in the South Pacific is to be sacrificed in an atomic test that will kill all

wildlife, destroy the island, and pollute the ocean. Hurry up and find your way to the bomb and pull the fuse.

HELP THE TURTLE

Some turtles are almost extinct. This sea turtle, hatched from an egg on land, must get to the ocean to survive. Help him past the many predators that lie in wait for him.

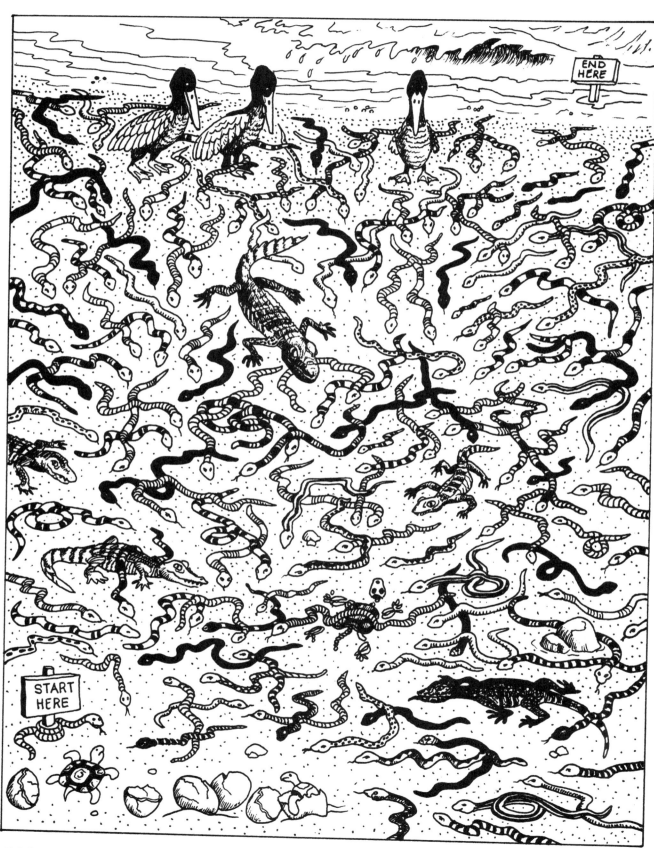

Wildlife

Many species of wildlife throughout the world are endangered because of the carelessness of man and because of shrinking environments. Man must intervene and become actively involved to save some species. The following mazes present some of the problems and give you a chance to help.

HELP THE DUCK FAMILY

This mallard drake and hen want to return their young to the nest. Help them find a clear channel to the nest.

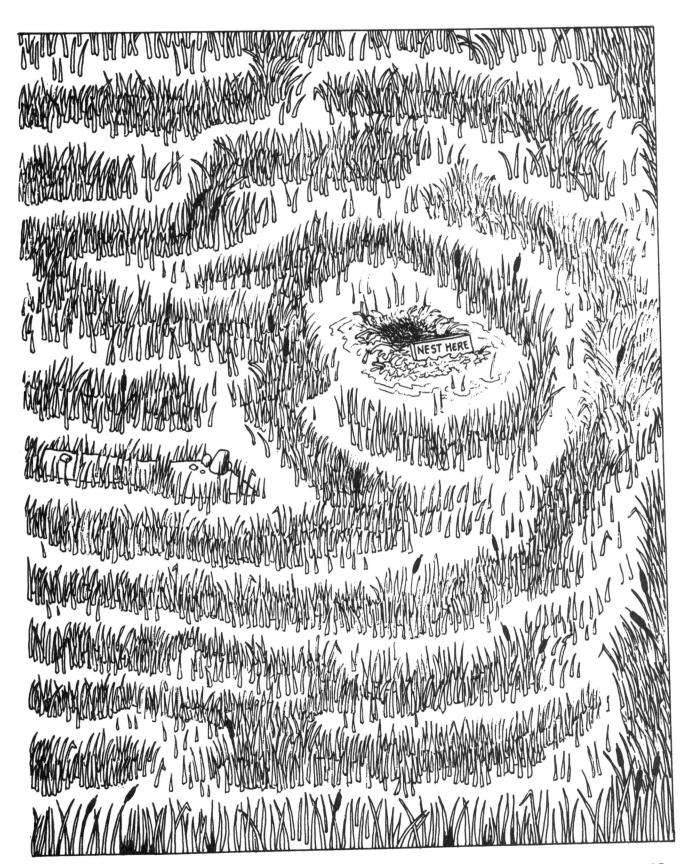

WATERPONDS FOR WATERFOWL

Migrating waterfowl need waterponds to feed and rest in. Waterponds across the country have been disappearing every year. This farmer will let you dig a waterpond

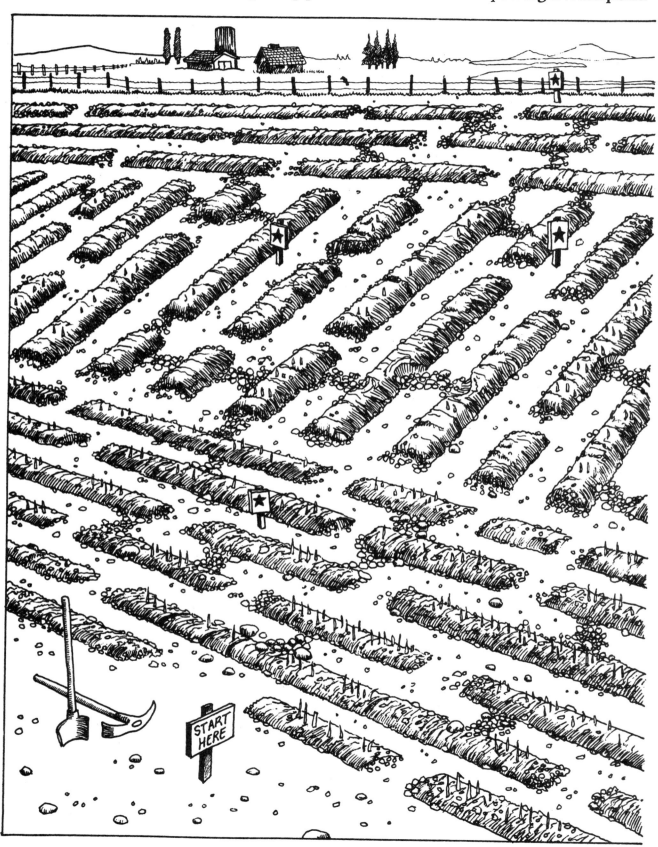

at each place he has put a star sign. Find a clear path and dig a pond at each sign. Do not backtrack. When you get to the water valve, flood the field to fill the ponds.

SAVE THE SPOTTED OWL

Save this family of spotted owls by finding a clear path to them and take them to an uncut forest.

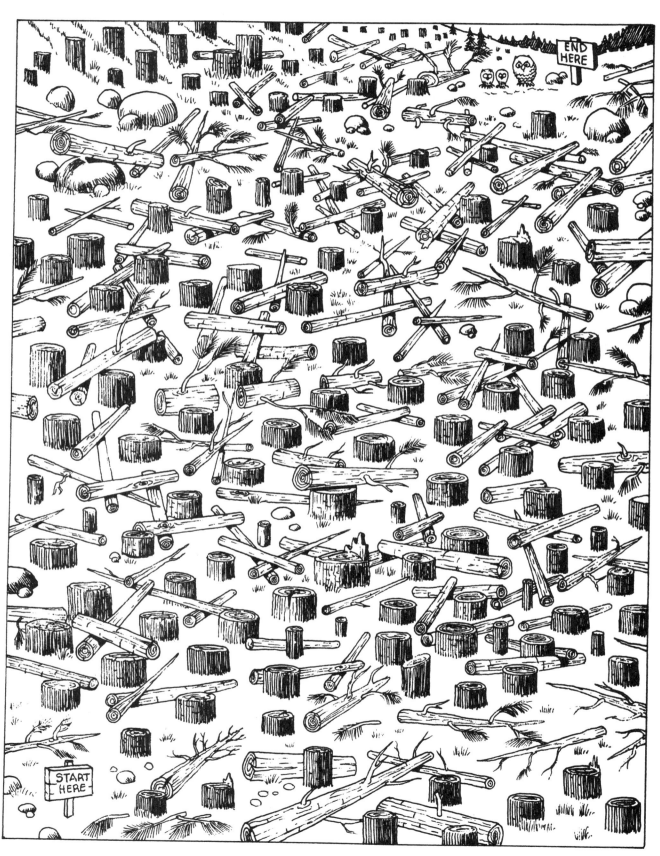

FEED THE BABY EAGLES

Every eagle is a treasure. These babies have lost their mother. Find a clear path up the trail, climb the tree, and feed them.

SAVE THE ELEPHANTS AND RHINOS

Animals with ivory tusks are endangered and are protected from hunting. But poachers, men who hunt against the law, try to kill them to sell the ivory. Another

START
HERE

SAWS

SAWS

way to protect these animals is to cut off their ivory tusks. This does not hurt the animal, and they will not be hunted. Save the elephant and rhinos by finding a clear path to them and cut off their tusks.

ARREST THE POACHER

This mountain gorilla is in grave danger. A poacher waits in hiding. Find a clear path and arrest the poacher.

SAVE THE RAIN FOREST

This rain forest is in danger of being cut down. Cutting down the rain forests

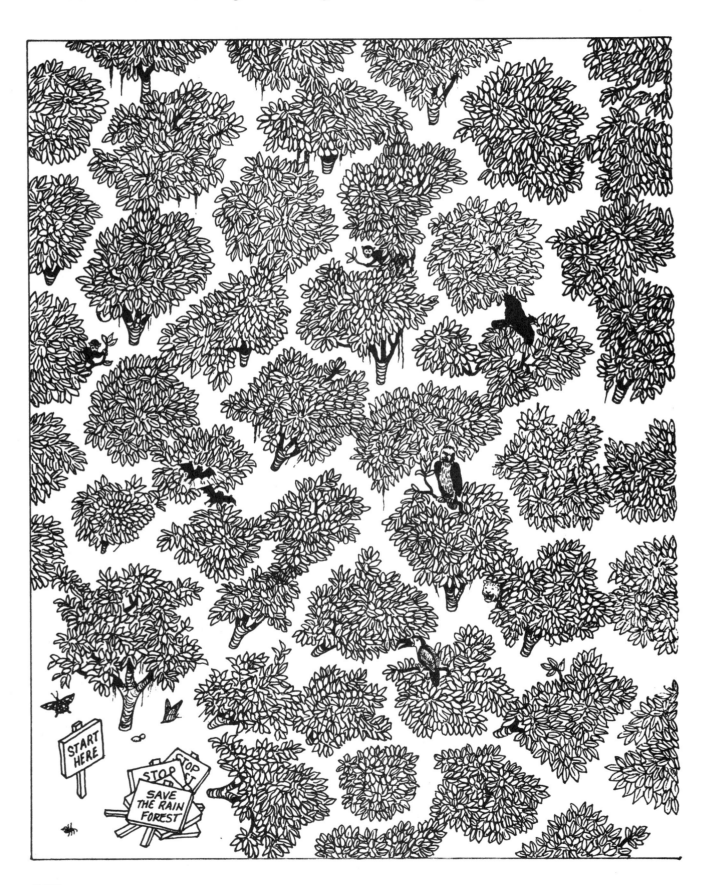

threatens life on the entire planet. Find a clear path and put these signs where the cutting crew has left their saws.

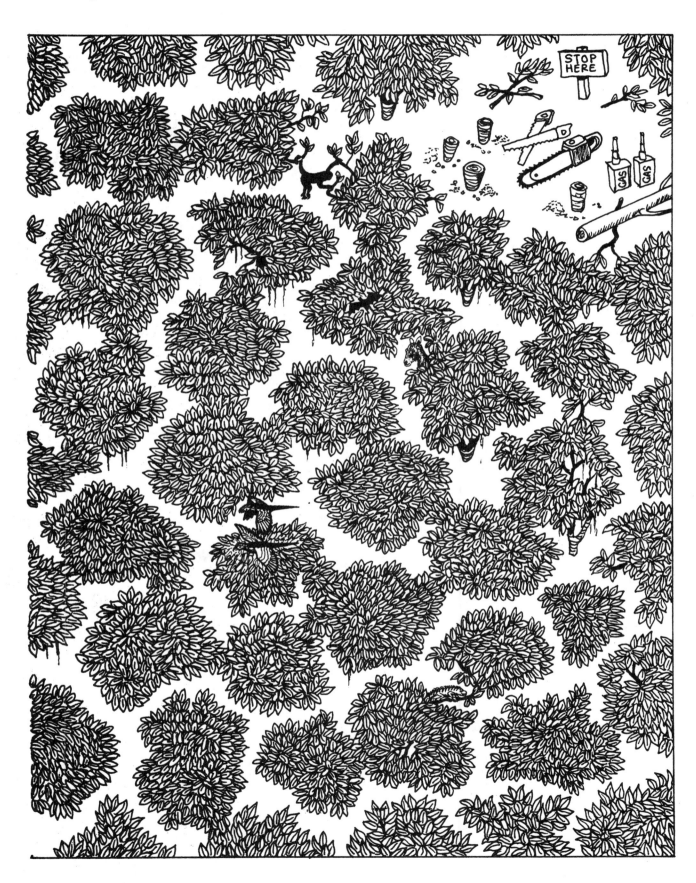

SAVE THE PANDA

Pandas are almost extinct because they are slow to get together and produce

offspring. They sometimes die off faster than they reproduce. Help this male panda find a clear path to the female in the upper right.

SAVE THE CALIFORNIA CONDOR

Only a few California condors exist, raised in captivity. Some have been released into the wild. Help them survive. Find a clear path to the cave and leave the condor food.

Pollution

Man's carelessness has polluted the earth so much that man himself is in danger. We dump and spill pollutants into the water and onto the land. Acid rain is caused by pollutants that get into the air and fall back to earth in the rain. These pollutants kill fish and wildlife. We must stop pollution and clean things up if we are to survive.

FIGHT THE OIL SPILL

This oil spill is a big mess. To save the birds and seal that are covered with oil, you must quickly find a clear path through the mess.

STOP ACID RAIN

The white bricks stick out just enough from this pollutant spewing chimney so you can climb to the top and put a filter on it. Climb only on the connecting white bricks.

STOP NUCLEAR WASTE DUMPING

These trucks are going to dump radioactive waste into the canyon. Get up the trail in a hurry and stop them. Time is short. Hopefully, you'll be right the first time.

CLEAN UP THE PARK

The junk littering this once beautiful picnic area needs to be hauled away, but the removal truck is broken down. Find a clear path through the field and fix the truck.

STOP LAKE POLLUTION

This pipe is leaking toxic, industrial waste. Put the cork in it to stop the pollution of

this freshwater lake. As you row, find your way through clean white water. Do not get any pollution on you or the boat.

PRODUCE FRESH DRINKING WATER

Place clean ice blocks from the high mountains into the funnel and find your way down the pipes to open the valve and fill the bottles. It is OK to go behind other pipes.

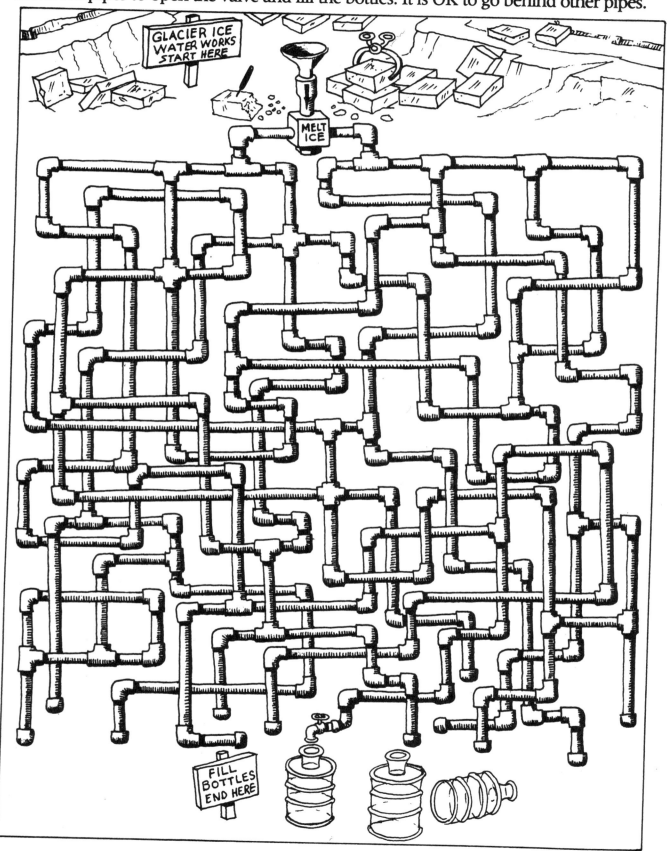

STOP AIR POLLUTION

A van on this freeway is polluting the air. Take the patrol car and arrest the driver. Be careful you don't get off on the wrong freeway.

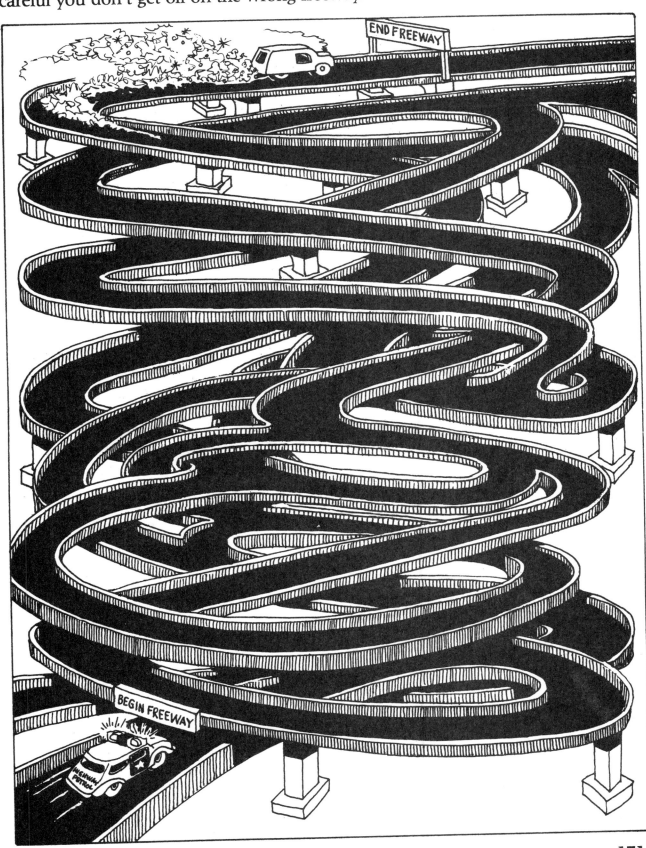

Congratulations!

Mother Earth thanks you for a job well done. You have come to understand that she is fragile and that her problems are very serious. More than two billion people throughout the world lack safe drinking water. Increased carbon dioxide, methane, and other gases in our atmosphere could have disastrous consequences. Scientists have estimated that 1.2 million species of animals will vanish during the next quarter century. It is a fact that it will take a worldwide collective effort to reverse such conditions if we are to save the Earth.

Some people have already started. Large-scale efforts have shown that soil erosion and land destruction can be stopped when a real effort is made. Tropical forests do not have to be leveled in order to feed people.

We have all the resources we need to start bringing our world into balance with nature. Many countries have been increasing their efforts to recycle waste, eliminate air pollution, and manage natural resources. The situation is not hopeless.

To save the Earth, it takes people who have courage, strength, self-motivation, and a desire to be part of the solution—not part of the problem. You have demonstrated, through your efforts in this book, that you have these characteristics and concerns. As you work to rebuild the world, know that the time has come. Be a leader and encourage others to follow your example.

Good luck.

Help for Earth Savers

The world's problems are difficult. It is not unlikely that you could have run into some problems along the way. If you need help or want to check how you did, the keys to the mazes follow.

Save the Dolphin

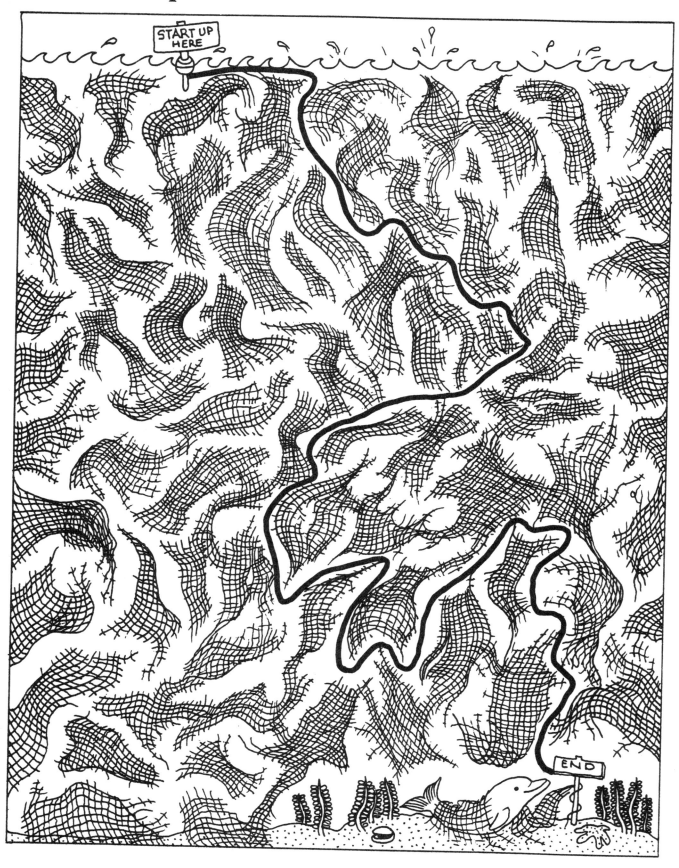

Free the Fishes

Free the Whale

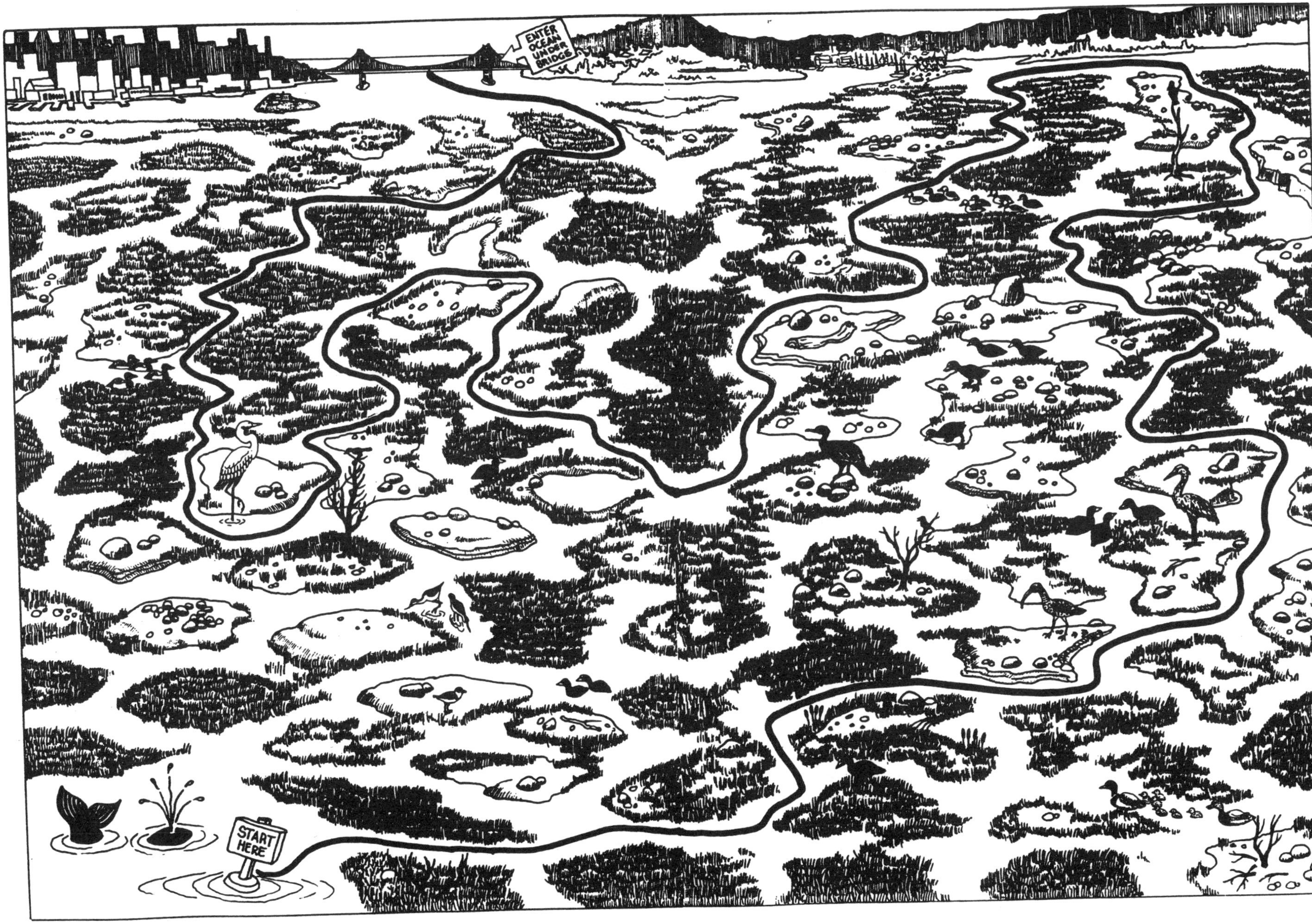
ENTER OCEAN UNDER BRIDGE
START HERE

Help the Duck Family

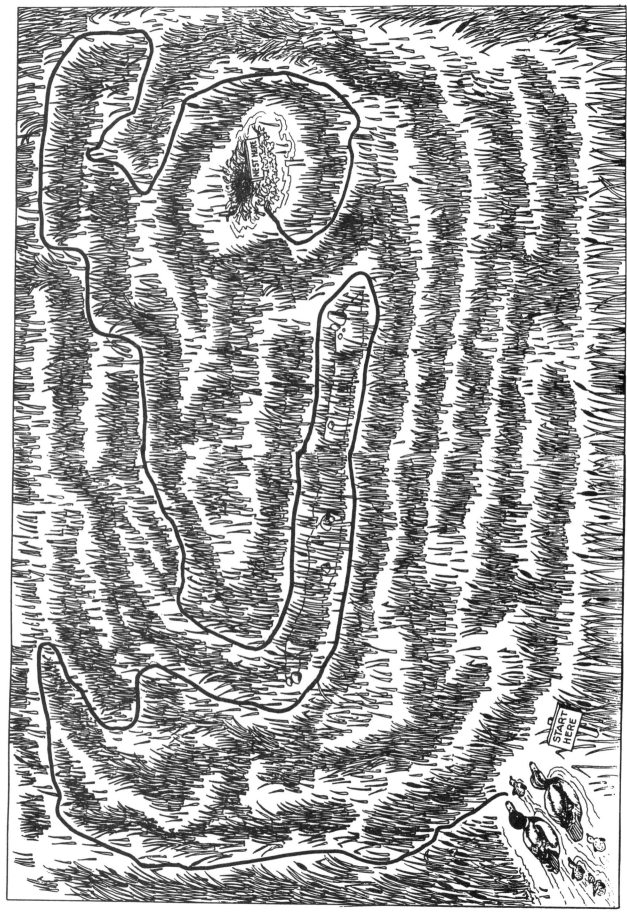

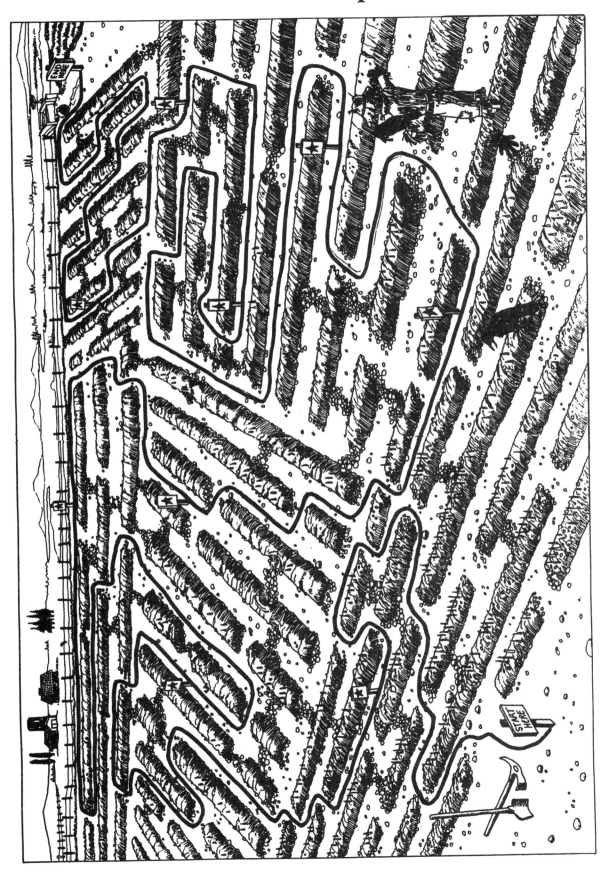

Save the Spotted Owl

ARREST POACHER HERE →

START HERE

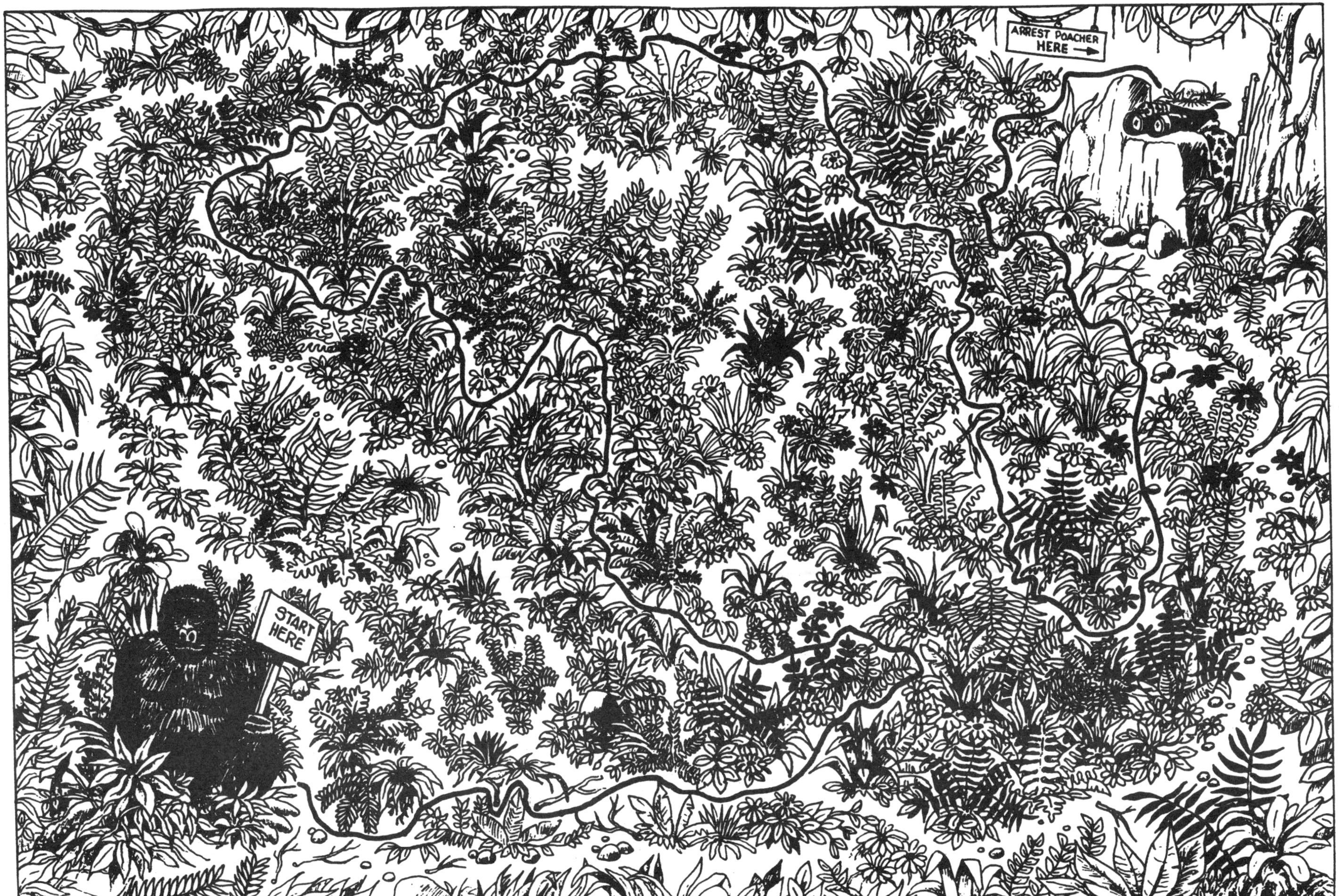

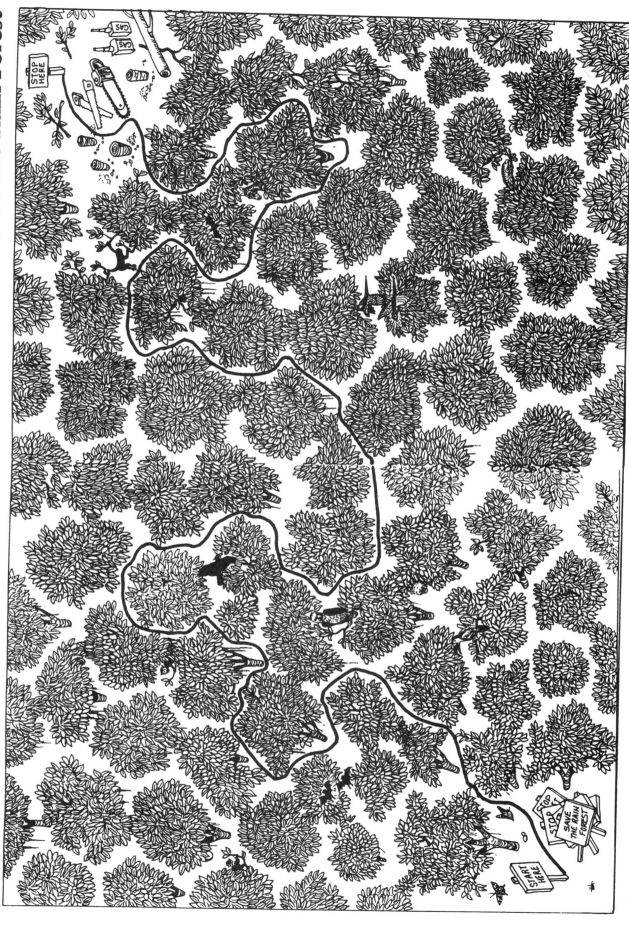

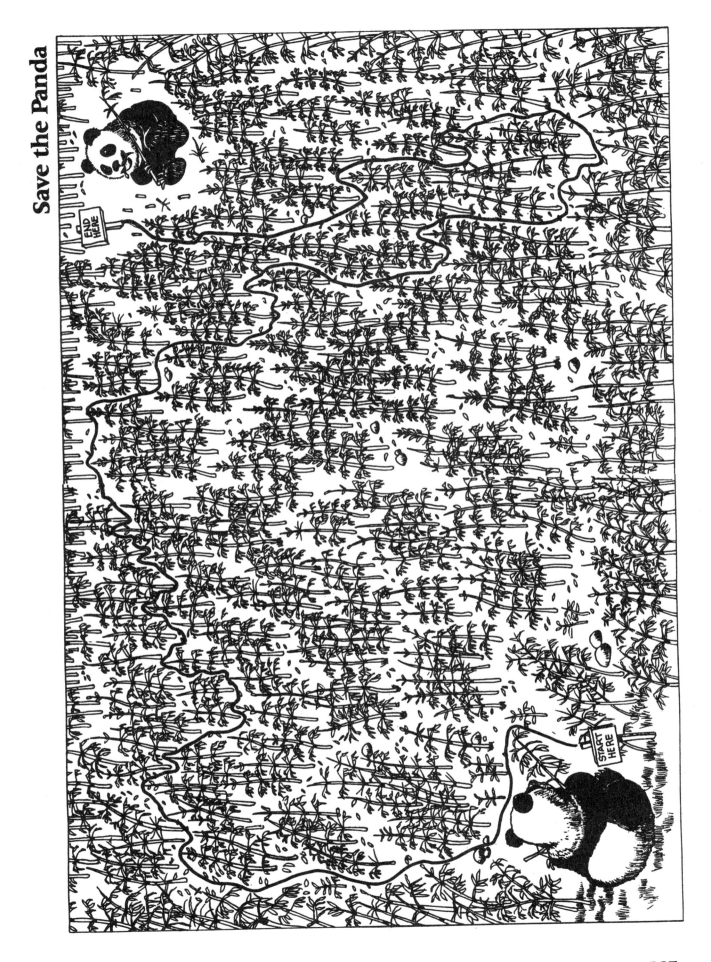

Save the California Condor

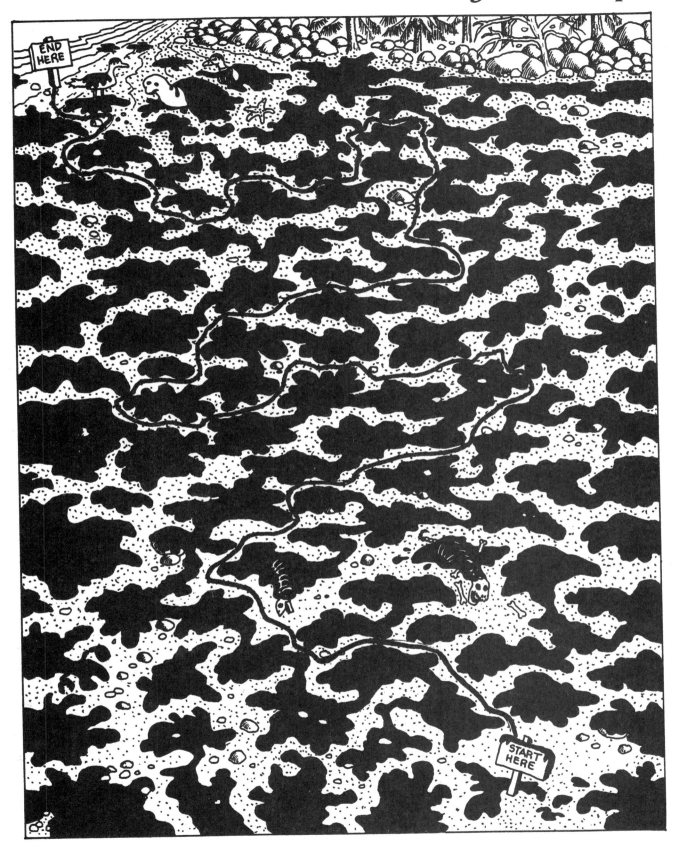

Stop Acid Rain

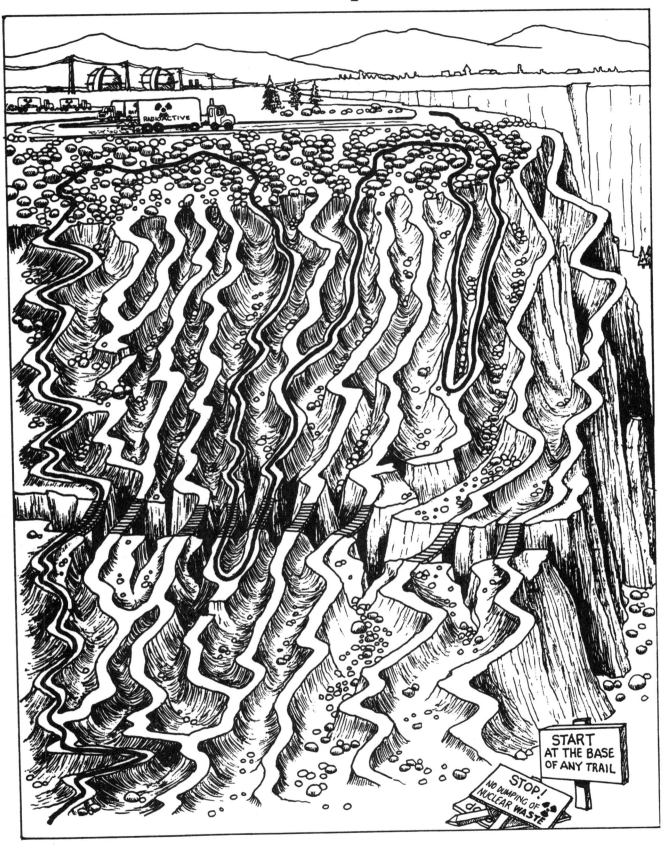

Clean Up the Park

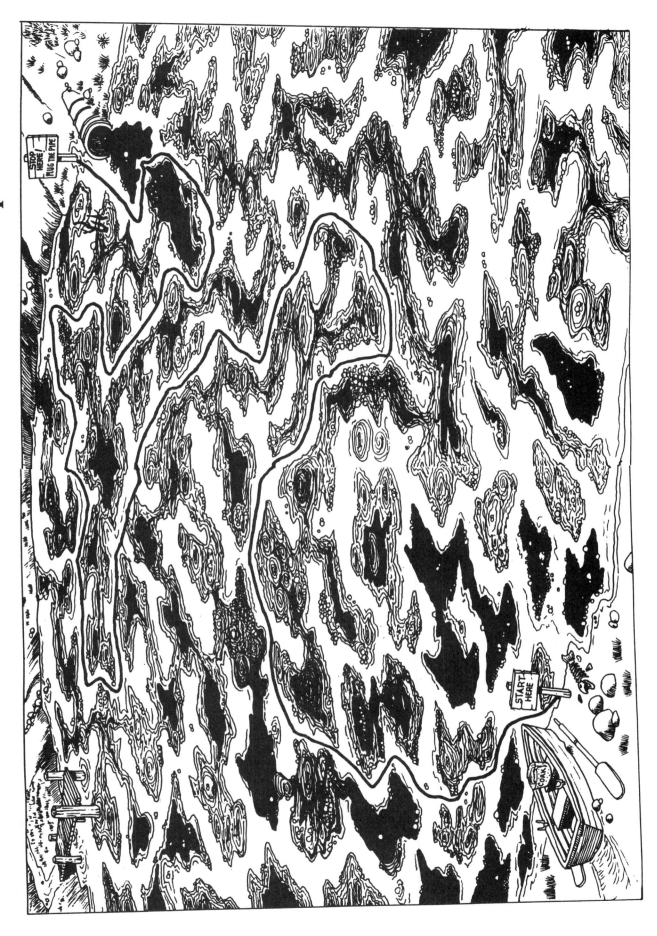

Produce Fresh Drinking Water

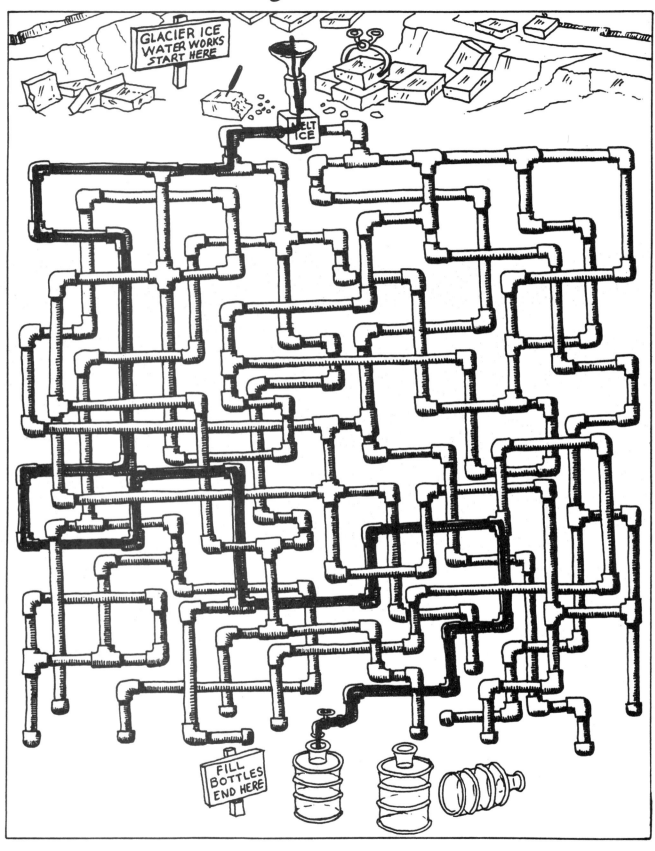

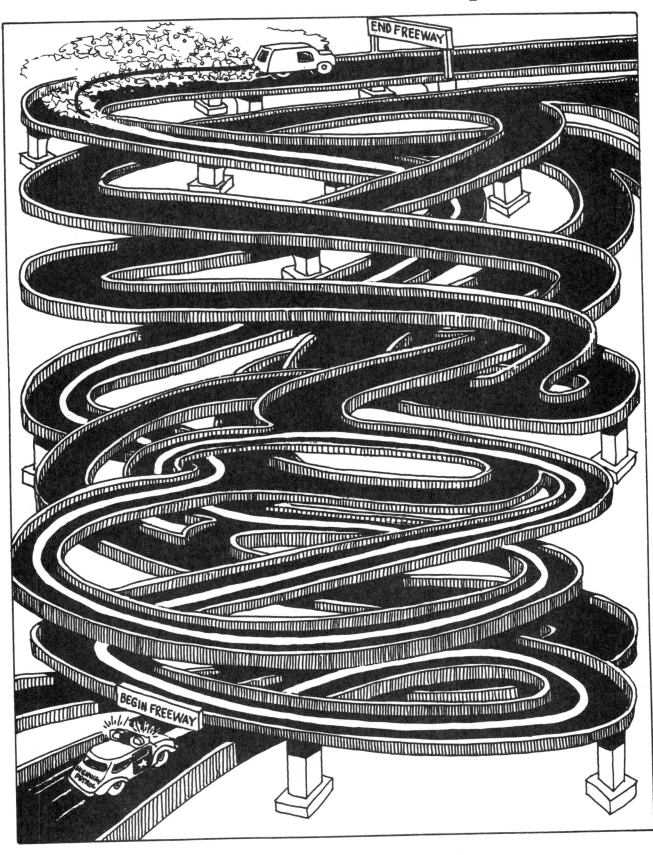

Jungle Mazes

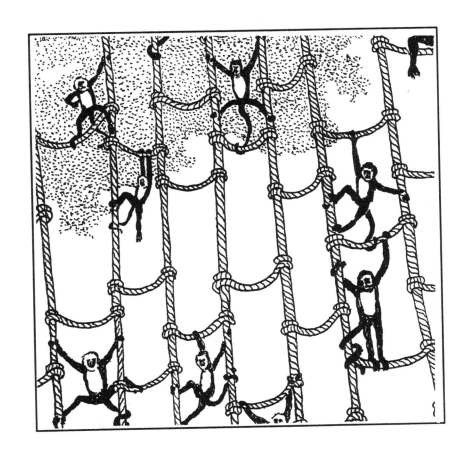

CONTENTS

The Jungles of Central and South America 266

Starting Up the Amazon 267
Alligator Alley 268
The Top of the Rain Forest 269
The World of Birds 270
The Frog Pond 272
The Butterfly Chase 274
Stalking the Jaguar 276

The Jungles of Africa 278

The Road to the Jungle 279
The Gorilla Family 280
Spiders, Spiders 282
The Golden Potto 284
Jungle Photo Trip 285
The Elephant Herd 286
Monkey Business 288

The Jungles of Southeast Asia 290

A Clear Path 291
The Temple of Angkor 292
Inside the Temple 294
Snakes and Roots 296
Looking for Lizards 297
The Crossroads 298

Jungle Guides 300

INTRODUCTION

The great imaginary circle around the earth that lies halfway between the North and South poles is known as the equator. Here, days and nights are always of almost equal length, about 12 hours each along the equator. In most regions, the temperatures are hot and humid. Here are found the great rain forests, or jungles, of the world—in Central and South America, Africa, and Southeast Asia. One third of the world's land, or 15 million square miles, is jungle.

These jungles are filled with an abundant variety of friendly and unfriendly plants, insects, wildlife and people. The variety is so abundant that a great number of species are rarely seen and an equal number are still undiscovered. It is a fact that a lot of the known life benefits the human family in many ways. It needs to be protected and preserved.

A great deal still needs to be learned about these jungles. More exploration is needed. This is where the people of the world would like to call upon you. If you volunteer to go forth into the jungles ahead, it will be a great opportunity for you to do good for mankind. You will explore and photograph rare and unknown species. You will experience the thrill of discovery. It will be important for you to observe and note carefully the things that you see. But, be cautioned, it will require determination and uncommon courage. You will have to face much dangerous wildlife and many life-threatening situations.

GOOD LUCK!

THE JUNGLES OF CENTRAL AND SOUTH AMERICA

The jungles of Central and South America contain an enormous variety of plants and wildlife. It is believed that nearly one third of all the earth's species lives in these jungles. Many of these species remain unnamed and unknown. Now you are ready to seek out, observe and study some of rarest ones.

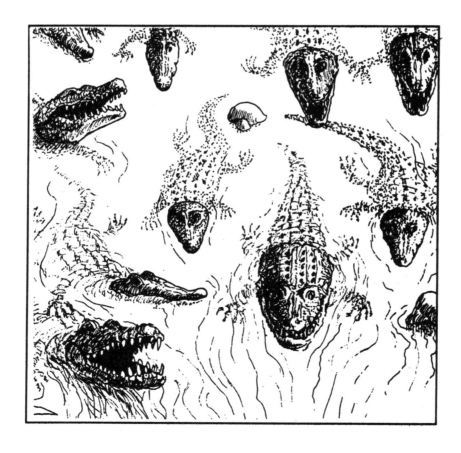

Starting Up the Amazon

To reach the jungle, start up the Amazon River by finding your way to where the river narrows.

Alligator Alley

Here, the river narrows and the anxious welcome that awaits you looks pretty dangerous. Avoid the alligators and work your way upstream and into the jungle.

The Top of the Rain Forest

This rain forest tree is full of wildlife. Ascend the vines to the top. You can move from vine to vine where they cross, but you must avoid disturbing the wildlife.

The World of Birds

There are many rare birds in these trees. Try to reach the unknown bird at the end

of this maze by ascending the vines and branches. You can move from vine to vine where they cross, but avoid vines blocked by birds.

The Frog Pond

This pond has several rare frogs in it and one that has never been seen before. You

can get to him by moving from lily pad to lily pad. They must be touching for you to advance. Don't worry about any frogs that are on lily pads and don't fall in.

The Butterfly Chase

Beautiful butterflies! Everyone loves butterflies. To get to that rare one on the

right, move along a single vine. You can go under and over other vines but you cannot move from one to another.

Stalking The Jaguar

The jaguar is an endangered species. You are lucky to have spotted two resting in

this tree. Work your way up the branches and get a photo. You can cross from branch to branch where they cross but not where leaves block the way.

THE JUNGLES OF AFRICA

Wildlife in the jungles of Africa is as abundant and varied as in Central and South America. It is also quite different. Zaire holds one-tenth of the world's total rain forest and in the remote regions of the Congo, the rain forests are virtually undisturbed by the encroachment of man.

The Road to the Jungle

To get to the jungle, hike down the road, avoiding the wildlife in the valley below.

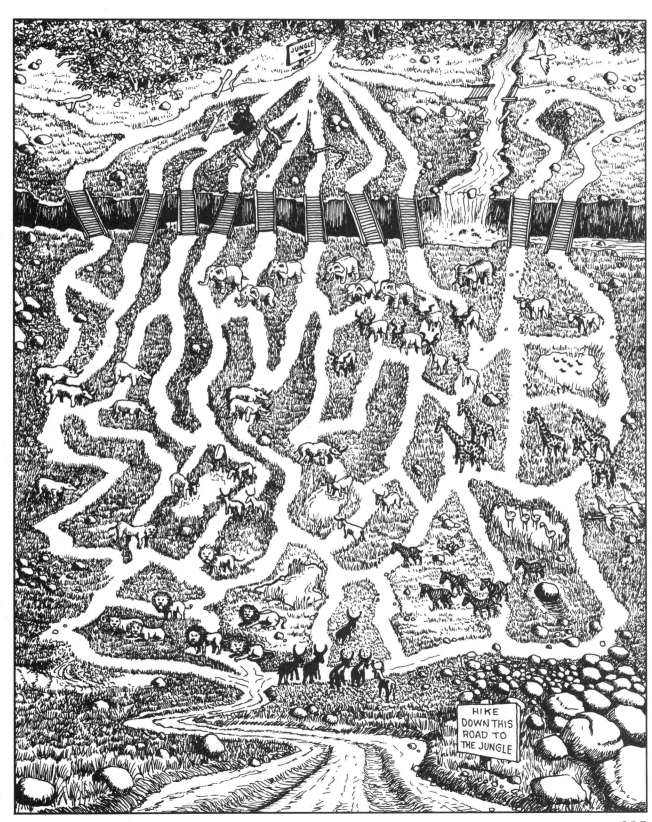

The Gorilla Family

That's the mother gorilla checking out your camera equipment and the father

overseeing the family and some of the neighbor's children. Get out your camera equipment, for a picture of the mother and continue up the trail to get one of the father. Do not disturb the children or the parents might not like it.

Spiders, Spiders

Spiders! Everyone hates spiders—except you. To observe that rare one in the

upper right, climb the spiderwebs by moving along where they are not blocked by spiders. Be careful not to get stuck on this maze. It could prove dangerous.

The Golden Potto

Study the rare Golden Potto by ascending the vines. You can cross from vine to vine and move along the branch at the top. Avoid the bugs.

Jungle Photo Trip

This is a real photo opportunity. Much of Africa's wildlife can been seen in this jungle area. Find a clear path to the top of the hill and don't save on film.

The Elephant Herd

That herd of elephants on the ridge appears to be unaware of you. But one big bull

START
HERE

is starting to charge down the hill. Wouldn't it be a great chance to observe, close up, a charging elephant? Find a clear path up the trail. You'd better hurry.

Monkey Business

To get up into this rain forest tree and observe the wildlife, you hung these ropes.

Do you think it was a good idea? It looks as if the monkeys and chimpanzees have taken over. Now you can't just climb any rope; you must avoid the monkeys and chimps to get up.

THE JUNGLES OF SOUTHEAST ASIA

The jungles of Southeast Asia are as unique and diversified as any of the jungles of the world. Some parts of New Guinea are so remote that they are rarely if ever explored. One can just imagine the variety of undiscovered like that most assuredly exists there. Many brave men have made attempts to find out. Some have returned to log their finds. Others were **never seen** again.

A Clear Path

If you have any misgivings about the jungle ahead, take heart. Notice that there is a welcome sign. All you have to do is find a clear path to entrance.

The Temple of Angkor

Visit the temple ruins of Angkor. The statues of the gods are overgrown with jungle

vines. To explore the temple, climb the vines. You can move along from vine to vine except where they are blocked by leaves.

Inside the Temple

Most of the roof of this temple has collapsed. Find a clear path and exit through the door at the far end.

Snakes and Roots

No matter how you feel about snakes, don't let this chance slip to observe that big one in the tree. Climb from root to root but avoid the other snakes at all costs.

Looking for Lizards

There's a lizard at the bottom of this hill. It looks pretty safe, so find a clear path down and get a photo. Keep your eyes open for any signs of danger.

The Crossroads

There seems to be a crossroads ahead where you must make an important decision

as to which way to go. It's up to you. But before you decide, look things over carefully. Either way, you must find a clear path.

CONGRATULATIONS

Your discoveries have been made and the photos you took will be studied for years. It is very likely that new cures and scientific breakthroughs will occur as a result of the sacrifices and hardships that you had to endure to achieve such great success. There is no question that during your expedition your life was in danger, and yet you did not give up. You did not quit when the going got tough. When you were lost, you found your way. It is apparent that you took your responsibilities seriously, because you were careful to observe the smallest details along the way. This was not easy, and yet you did it. In fact, you have done so well that you will probably be called on again for some future task, possibly more difficult than this.

JUNGLE GUIDES

If you had any trouble finding your way through the mazes in this book, use the jungle guides on the following pages. These guides should be used only in case of an emergency.

Alligator Alley

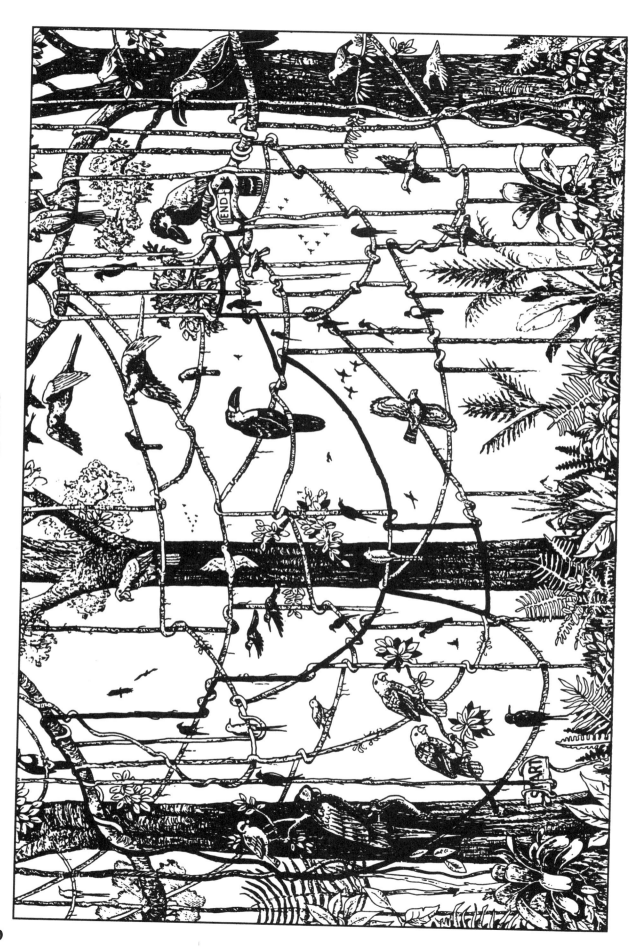

The Frog Pond

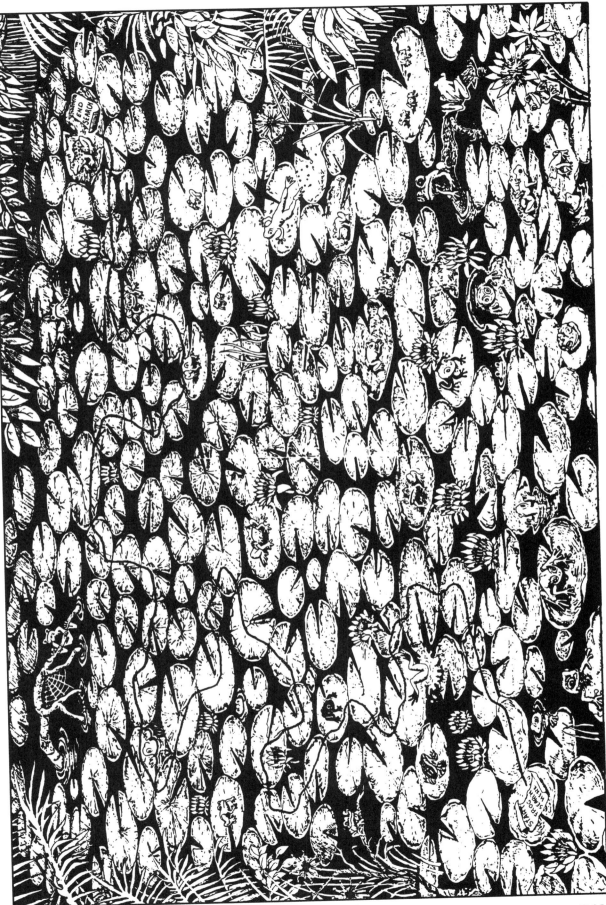

241

The Butterfly Chase

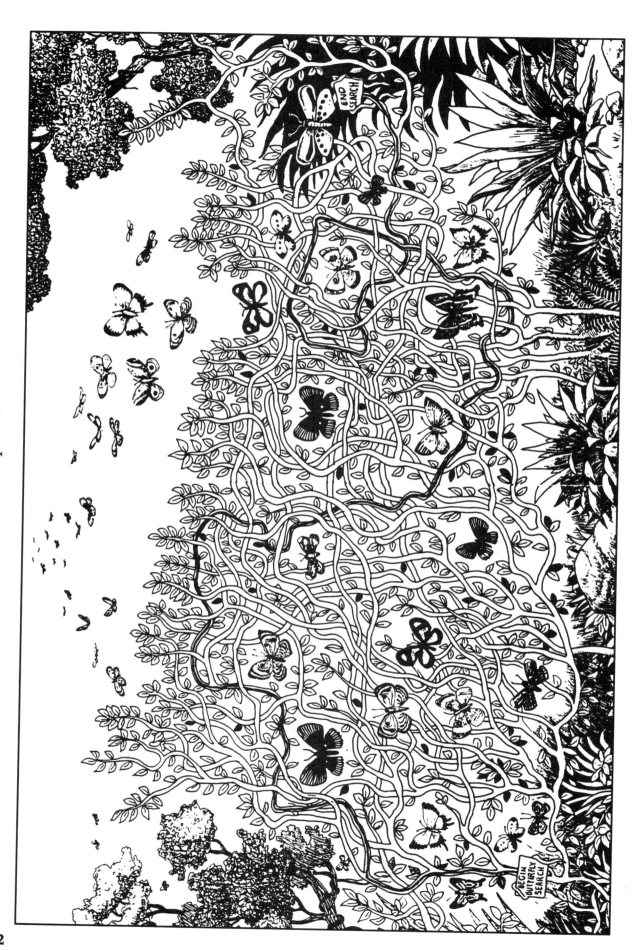

Stalking The Jaguar

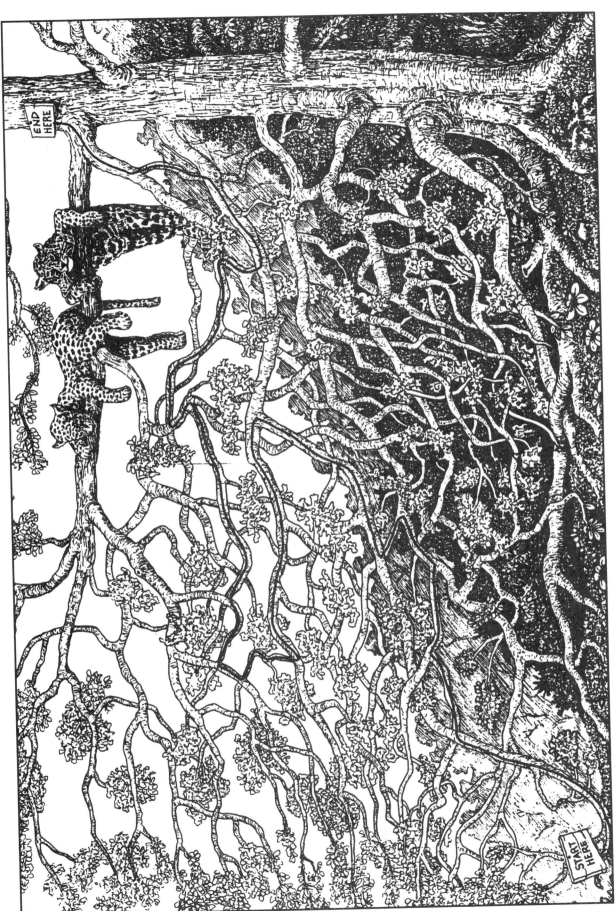

The Road to the Jungle

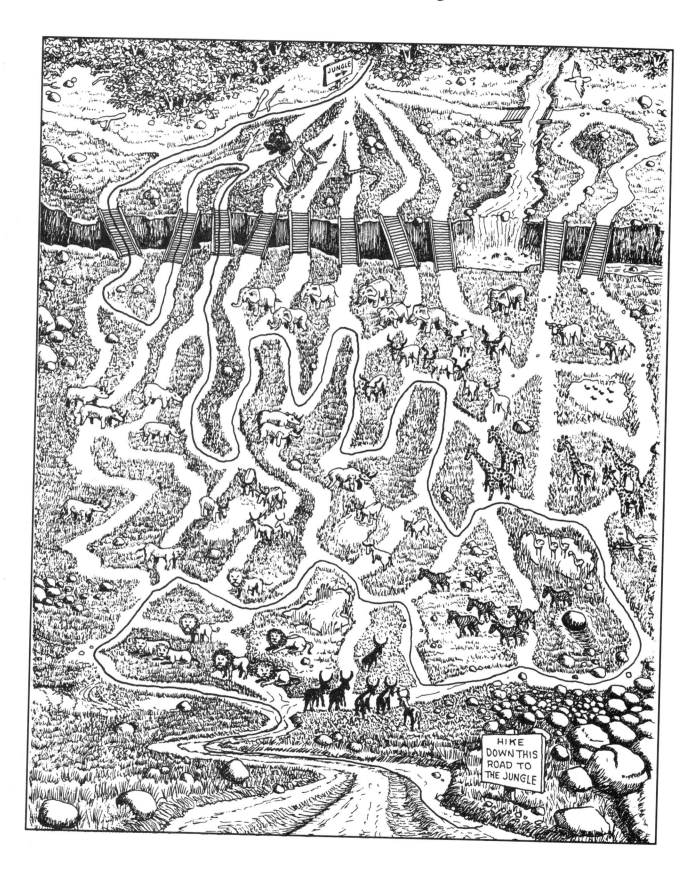

The Gorilla Family

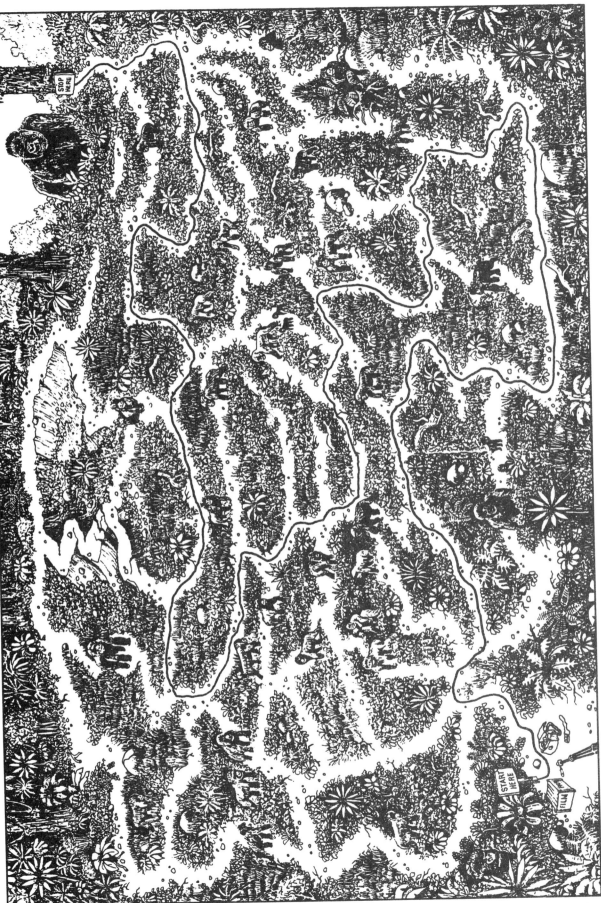

245

Spiders, Spiders

The Golden Potto

Jungle Photo Trip

The Elephant Herd

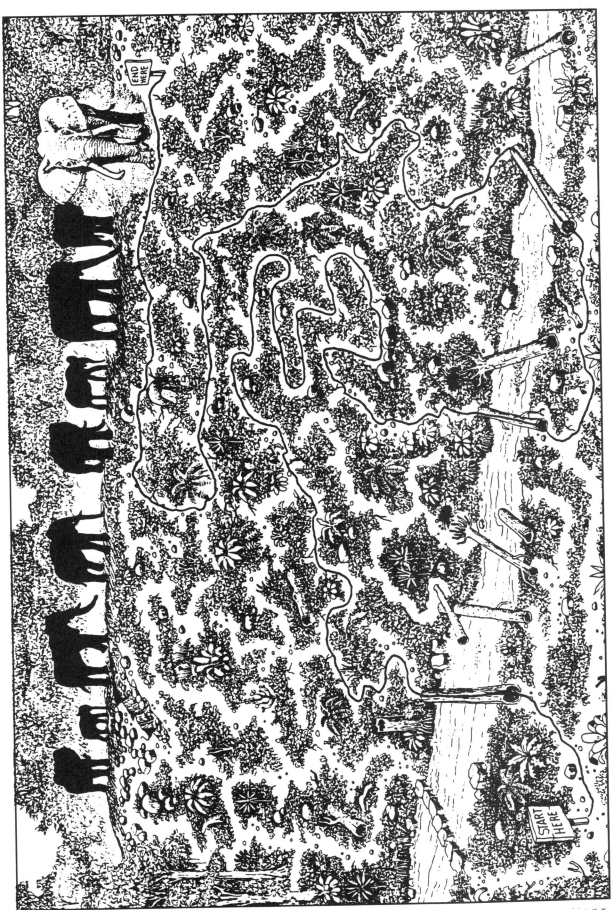

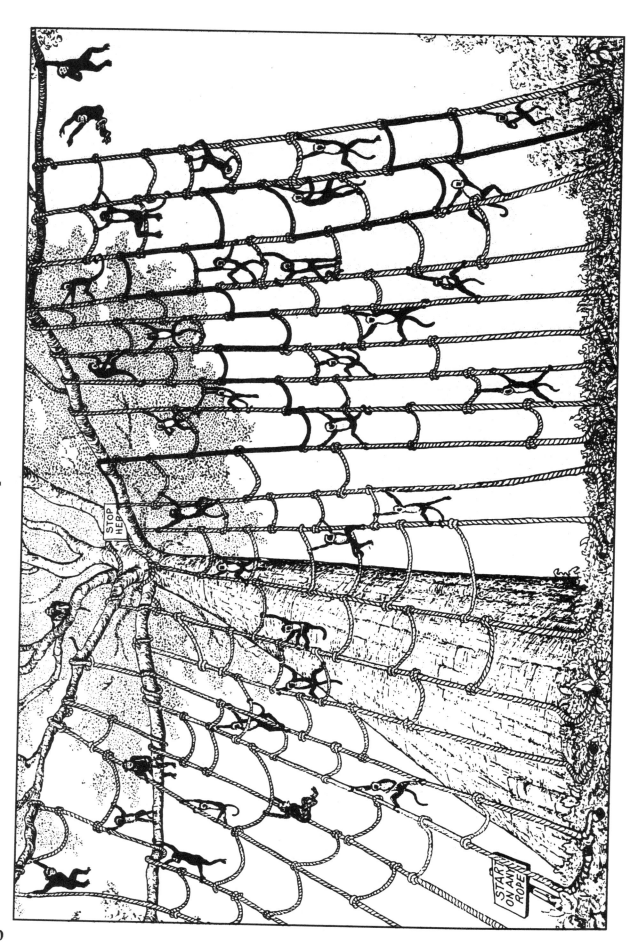

Monkey Business

The Temple of Ankor

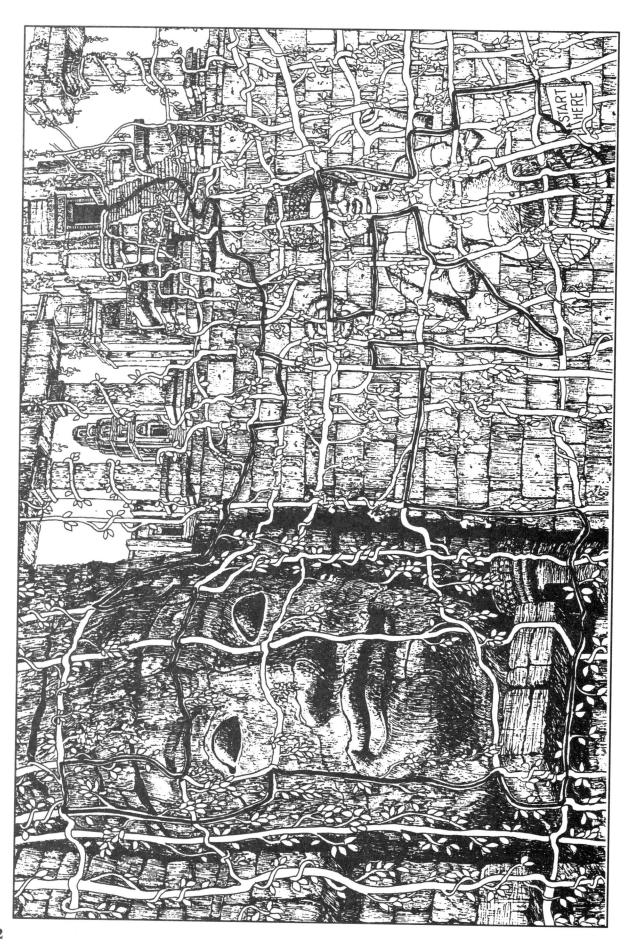

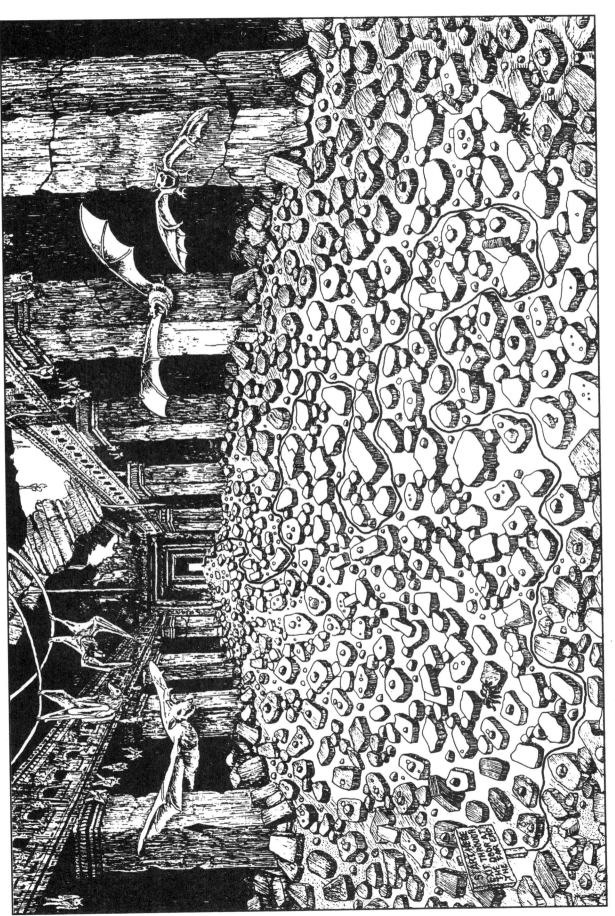

Snakes and Roots

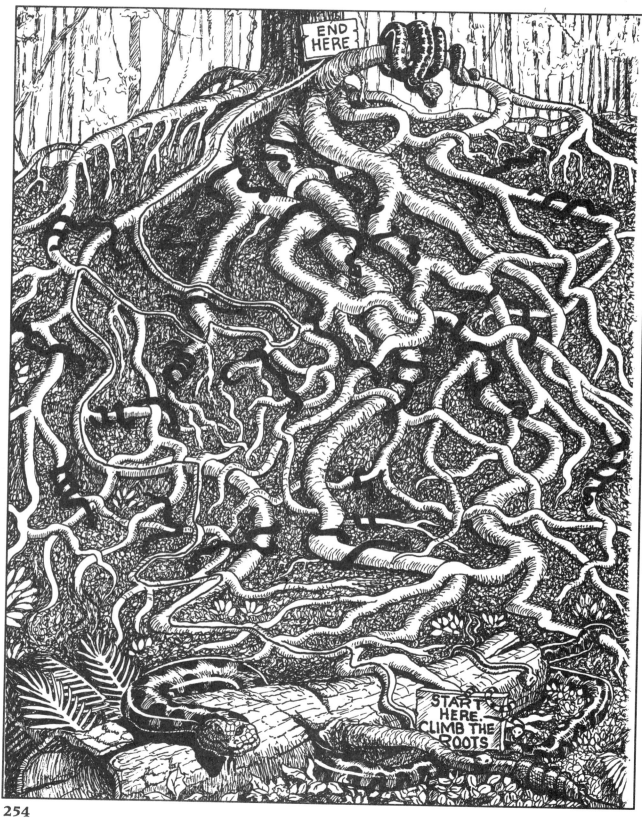

Looking for Lizards

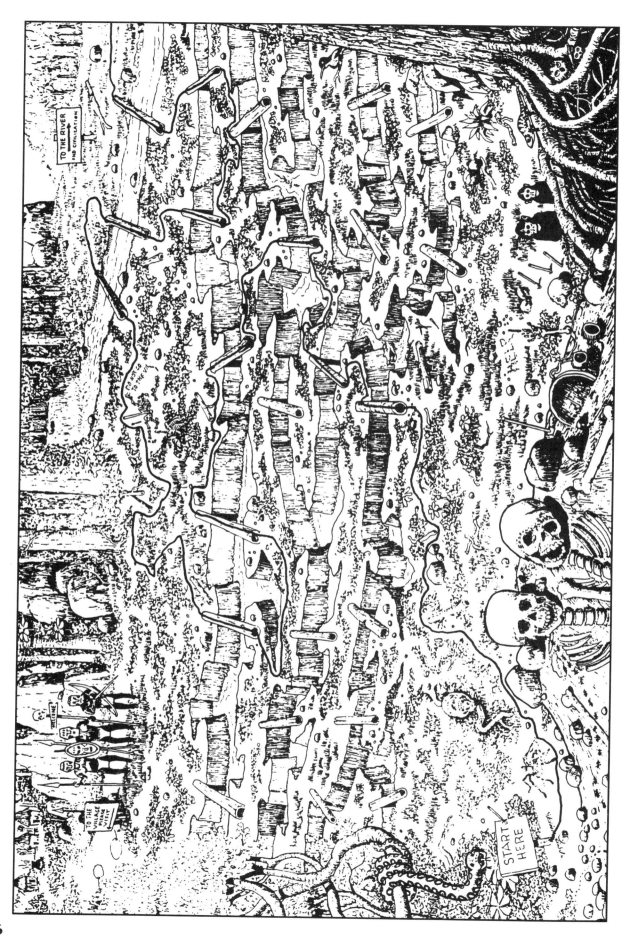

The Giant Book of
Word Search
Puzzles

A MAIN STREET BOOK

10 9 8 7 6 5 4 3 2 1

Published in 2000 by Sterling Publishing Company, Inc.
387 Park Avenue South, New York, N.Y. 10016

Copyright © 2000 Sterling Publishing Company, Inc.
Suits Me Fine © 1999 by Mark Dana
Interior design & copy production by Mulberry Tree Press, Inc.
(MulberryTreePress.com)

Distributed in Canada by Sterling Publishing
c/o Canadian Manda Group
One Atlantic Avenue, Suite 105
Toronto, Ontario, Canada M6K 3E7

Dsitributed in Great Britain and Europe by Cassell PLC
Wellington House, 125 Strand
London WC2R)BB, United Kingdom

Distributed in Australia by Capricorn Link (Australia) Pty Ltd.
P.O. Box 6651, Baulkham Hills, Business Centre,
NSW 2153, Australia

Manufactured in the United States of America.

Contents

Card Games 4

Transportation 6

Things That Fly 8

Space 10

Airplane Parts 12

Boats 14

Airports 16

Car Parts 18

Car Racing 20

Countries of Africa 22

Animals of Africa 24

Animals of Australia 26

Cities and Towns
    of Australia 28

Birds of North America 30

Mexico 32

Capitals of Europe 34

Scandinavia 36

Spain 38

Switzerland 40

France 42

Greece 44

Italy 46

Capitals of States
    and Provinces 48

Caribbean and
    the West Indies 50

Egypt 52

Languages 54

Languages of Asia 56

Fish 58

Wild West 60

Oceania 62

Basketball Players 64

Baseball 66

Basketball 68

Bowling 70

Football 72

Golf 74

Martial Arts 76

Emmy Awards 78

Famous Actors 80

Famous Actresses 82

Skiing 84

Tennis 86

Track and Field 88

Artist 90

Beach 92

Camp 94

Classic Books 96

Collectibles 98

Evening News 100

Exercise 102

Fishing 104

Music 106

Photography 108

Slumber Party 110

That's Sharp 112

Tools 114

Dance 116

Fabric 118

Green 120

Red 122

Halloween 124

Thanksgiving 126

Christmas 128

Valentine's Day 130

Fourth of July 132

Anybody Thirsty? 134

Barbecue 136

Bread 138

Breakfast 140

Desserts 142

Pies 144

Sundaes 146

Diner Food 148

Fruit 150

Herbs 152

Nuts 154

Vegetables 156

What's on the Table? 158

In the Bathroom 160

In the Bedroom 162

Get Dressed 164

Gems 166

In the Kitchen 168

It's Cold 170

It's Hot 172

Jewelry 174

Clean Up 176

In the Living Room 178

Family 180

Flowers 182

Garden 184

School Time 186

Begins with "cla..." 188

Begins with "gra..." 190

Begins with "pla..." 192

Presidents of
    the United States 194

Trees 196

Constellations 198

Measurements 200

Insects 202

Sharks 204

Mammals 206

Wild Cats 208

Mythical Creatures 210

Academy Awards 212

At the Movies 214

Musical Instruments 216

Art & Entertainment
    Magazines 218

Newspapers 220

Sports Magazines 222

Fashion & Style Magazines 224

Suits Me Fine 227

ANSWER KEYS 228

Card Games

ACCORDION	JAMBOREE
BLACKJACK	LOTTERY
BRIDGE	MONTE
CALCULATION	PAIRS
CANASTA	PATIENCE
CASINO	PICQUET
CRIBBAGE	PINOCHLE
EUCHRE	POKER
FARO	REVERSE
FRIGHT	RUMMY
FROG	SKAT
GO FISH	SOLITAIRE

```
D  T  W  W  G  E  G  H  N  A  Y  M  E  M
O  H  K  W  W  O  T  S  N  B  R  Y  O  E
N  G  P  D  E  B  R  I  D  G  E  N  K  S
E  I  A  W  F  D  Y  F  Q  I  T  P  R  R
E  R  I  A  T  I  L  O  S  E  T  P  G  E
Y  F  R  A  C  E  G  G  E  S  O  B  P  V
M  O  S  T  A  C  L  R  H  K  L  D  I  E
M  C  A  S  I  N  O  H  E  A  K  M  C  R
U  E  G  A  B  B  I  R  C  T  S  N  Q  H
R  M  S  N  M  Y  D  K  D  O  E  Q  U  C
O  O  B  A  P  U  J  Z  P  I  N  W  E  U
B  X  J  C  R  A  F  E  T  F  O  I  T  E
T  C  A  L  C  U  L  A  T  I  O  N  P  X
J  R  U  K  B  W  P  N  I  A  H  W  K  Z
```

5

Transportation

AIRPLANE	JET SKI
BICYCLE	MONORAIL
BIKE	MOTORCYCLE
BOAT	ROCKET
BUGGY	SCOOTER
BUSES	SKATES
CABLECAR	SKIS
CANOE	SLED
CARS	SNOWMOBILE
FEET	TAXI
HELICOPTER	TRACTOR
HORSE	TRAIN

```
F Y G G U B A H N M Q G P I
D H F G U U P S J E T S K I
X H S S G J H X L B A E F D
C D E R S B M C T B X T E P
H S M L A C Y A F X I A P F
C H E L I C O P T E R K I Q
B D Q R R B E O L N V S E L
U H T O P I O L T M I V I S
I H T R L C D M B E H A D T
D O Z J A Y O B W A R S R A
M R F N N C Z I R O C K E T
Z S O E E L T O N H N I X I
P E V E F E I O B W I S D T
O U T G Q B M I R S K A A L
```

7

Things That Fly

AIRPLANE

ARROW

BALLOON

BATS

BIRDS

BLIMP

BOOMERANG

BROOM

BULLET

BUTTERFLY

FLAG

FLIES

FRISBEE

GLIDER

HELICOPTER

JAVELIN

JUMBO JET

KITE

MISSILE

MOSQUITO

MOTH

ROCKET

SHUTTLE

SPACESHIP

```
I R J H J F Q L A H E C Q E
W P N Q B O O M E R A N G H
Q T S H U T T L E W R W T S
U O E T M L I I I K N O D R
O Y L J A C V E U M M R W H
L L C S O B D L E Q I O C F
M F B P Z B R U B B S C J V
O R T A G U M O T L S O N O
O E K C L L W U C F I I M I
R T S E I L F F J K L M R I
B T C S D E O A A E E A P F
N U S H E T L O V C E T G N
V B A I R P L A N E H E I U
H K S P Z Z J B E K A P G K
```

9

Space

AEROSPACE	GRAVITY
APOLLO	LAUNCH
ARMSTRONG	MISSION
ASTRONAUT	NASA
ASTRONOMY	PLANETS
COSMOS	ROCKET
DEEP	SATELLITE
DISCOVERY	SCIENCE
ECLIPSE	SHUTTLE
EXPLORE	SKYLAB
GEMINI	SOLAR
GLENN	STARS

```
H C N C E W W R O C K E T O
T S A L A C B B F K C T G L
Z U S N N E L G R A V I T Y
S R A T S G S I P R A L O S
N E C N E I C S P M K L J D
X Y Y M O N O R T S A E C C
O G I R I R A E H T E T U O
C N S R E S T L R R C A E S
I D K A Q V S S P O S S L M
O O D P S K O I A N L A T O
R D E O Y V X C O G U P I S
H E E L T T U H S N B P X Q
D B A L K I Z O C I K E Q E
I B U O U S Y H E D D W Q H
```

11

Airplane Parts

AFTERBURNER

AIRFOIL

BRAKE

CABIN

CHASSIS

COCKPIT

CONTROLS

DECK

EJECTOR

ENGINES

FLAP

FUSELAGE

HATCH

INSTRUMENTS

KEEL

NOSEWHEEL

RADAR

RUDDER

SPOILER

STABILIZER

TAIL

TURRET

WHEELS

WINGS

```
I H W E K E G A L E S U F M
T N W V D F L T E R R U T N
R G S E N I G N E I J S J X
E H C T A H B D H R L O K O
S K R T R W D G W E L J C Z
O R E N R U B R E T F A K D
R L Z J R M M H S C B Y A L
K E I G E T W E O I S L V Z
F E L O U C E N N W I N G S
B K I I F O T I E T S X E Y
W Z B L O R R O O K S I Q A
F Q A J O P I E R R A D A R
S P T L P W S A F S H R Q J
P F S L T I P K C O C D B U
```

13

Boats

BEACH

BOAT

CABIN

CANOE

CAPTAIN

CATAMARAN

CREW

CRUISE

DESTROYER

FISHING

KAYAK

LAKE

MOTOR

OCEAN

PONTOON

RAFT

RIVER

ROWING

SAILING

SEA

SHIP

SKIING

SUBMARINE

WAVES

```
M K F W D K A R Q J J J N N
P G O N A E C O C Z E O A X
P N N Y I V B R D U T P M Q
S B A K N B E F Q I T W E F
V K M B O W A S O F O Z N F
H R I O O E C C A P T A I N
C V E I T A H R L S R S R M
V S A Y N O T X U A H T A M
F T O O O G R G M I K E M Y
S K E F P R X A N L S E B S
Y G N X E N T G R I U E U N
W D L V C A P S G N W H S C
S H I P C P F U E G B O K S
V R T M L C H L L D D C R T
```

15

Airports

BEN GURION	LAGUARDIA
BISHOP	LAMBERT
BRADLEY	LOGAN
DE GAULLE	LUKOU
DORVAL	MCGHEE TYSON
DULLES	MIDWAY
EURO	MIRABEL
GATWICK	ORLY
HARTSFIELD	REAGAN
HEATHROW	SCHIPHOL
JOHN WAYNE	SHANNON
KENNEDY	SKY HARBOR

```
Y  E  C  H  W  Q  H  R  C  S  V  S  I  Y
I  U  D  D  U  O  K  U  L  G  P  O  L  M
J  R  T  R  B  S  R  M  L  A  V  R  O  D
N  O  S  Y  T  E  E  H  G  C  M  L  H  F
B  B  H  S  D  L  N  D  T  C  E  Y  P  M
I  R  L  N  A  L  A  G  U  A  R  D  I  A
S  A  A  N  W  U  E  M  U  Q  E  R  H  K
H  H  M  D  A  A  J  I  I  R  A  H  C  E
O  Y  B  U  L  G  Y  V  F  B  I  I  S  N
P  K  E  L  K  E  O  N  E  S  W  O  Z  N
A  S  R  L  I  D  Y  L  E  T  T  B  N  E
I  J  T  E  N  O  N  N  A  H  S  R  X  D
X  U  L  S  R  F  A  G  M  I  D  W  A  Y
Q  D  T  N  A  G  A  E  R  P  U  E  W  H
```

17

Car Parts

ACCELERATOR

ALTERNATOR

BELT

BRAKE

BUMPER

CARBURETOR

CHOKE

CLUTCH

CYLINDER

DASHBOARD

DIFFERENTIAL

GEARBOX

HEADLIGHT

HOOD

HORN

IGNITION

MIRROR

MUFFLER

PISTON

RADIATOR

SEAT

STARTER

VALVE

WINDSHIELD

```
F H C T U L C V B U M P E R
L E V X G F M A C F A K A N
C A Y Z N W U L F C O D L N
A D I T F O F V C H I W X Q
R L O T L K F E C A S I O I
B I T O N R L B T J B N B P
U G N E H E E O J P A D R V
R H O K R D R A O B H S A D
E T I A P N S E A T T H E V
T J T R C I A U F A L I G A
O O I B N L S T R F H E C S
R Q N E Q Y V T O B I L B O
U V G H M C E H O R N D E G
V C I R O R R I M N L M R Q
```

19

Car Racing

CRASH

DAYTONA

DRIVER

FORMULA ONE

GRAND PRIX

INDIANAPOLIS

MOTORSPORTS

NASCAR

POLE

POSITION

QUALIFYING

RACEWAY

RACING

RED FLAG

RESULTS

SAFETY

SEASON

SPEEDWAY

SPONSOR

TEAM

TRACK

VICTORY

WINNER

WRECK

```
E I G V J N S P E E D W A Y
S S N B B E O A G N I C A R
B P I D O S A N E O O P G O
G O Y E I G N O S A E S B T
R N F T H A N T T L L T V C
E S I Q S H N Y R U O R N I
N O L C A G R A O M P H P V
N R A G R A N D P R I X S Y
I R U B C L J D S O B C T H
W T Q E S F Q A R F L X L D
K R W U R D F X O I B I U Y
M A E T H E V L T L V L S V
Y C X C T R A G O H V E E B
K K S Y K T L Q M L F V R C
```

21

Countries of Africa

ALGERIA

ANGOLA

BENIN

BOTSWANA

CAMEROON

CONGO

EGYPT

ERITREA

ETHIOPIA

GHANA

GUINEA

KENYA

LIBERIA

LIBYA

MADAGASCAR

MALAWI

MALI

MOROCCO

MOZAMBIQUE

NAMIBIA

NIGERIA

SENEGAL

SUDAN

TANZANIA

TUNISIA

UGANDA

ZAMBIA

ZIMBABWE

```
L S U D A N E G Y P T W
I R X A I P O I H T E B
B A H Z G H A N A U E M
Y C I X I U A A Q N A A
A S C B R M I I I I B L
Y A A W I U B N R S R I
N G M N H M M A E I A B
E A E N A U A Z B A I E
K D R Z I W Z N L W R R
B A O Q P G S A G I E I
W M O V G O E T T O G A
O G N O C C O R O M L U
J L A G E N E S I B A A
U G A N D A M A L A W I
```

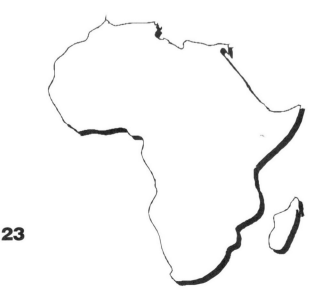

23

Animals of Africa

BABOON	HIPPOPOTAMUS
BONGO	HYENA
BUSHBUCK	IMPALA
CHEETAH	KUDU
CROCODILE	LEMUR
ELAND	LEOPARD
ELEPHANT	LION
FLAMINGO	OSTRICH
GAZELLE	PYTHON
GERENUK	SCORPION
GIRAFFE	STORK
GORILLA	ZEBRA

```
G E H N O H T Y P K P L
E L I D O C O R C T L E
R L P M G I R A F F E M
E E P E P O P C P F L U
N Z O F E A H R K D A R
U A P V L E L C O B N S
K G O R E A U A A C D T
A O T T P B M B P L S O
N M A D H X O I E Y R R
E H M S A O B O N G O K
Y N U Q N A P W O G R H
H B S N T A L L I R O G
E H C I R T S O L T Q B
T K U D U A R B E Z B I
```

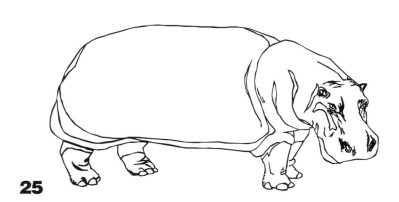

25

Animals of Australia

CHUDITCH	NUMBAT
DIBBLER	PARROT
DINGO	PLATYPUS
DJOONGARI	POSSUM
DOVE	POTOROO
ECHIDNA	QUOLL
FROG	SKINK
GLIDER	TORTOISE
KANGAROO	WALLABY
KOALA	WOMA
KOOKABURRA	WOMBAT
LYREBIRD	WOPILKARA

```
E T D O V E X G W W N C X A
K C M M U S S O P N K P D D
N X H I T D L I W O M A R R
I S D I D D J O O N G A R I
K G L I D E R K P T S B K B
S W C I B N A L I N R A G E
M O N H Z B A I L U N O E R
P G O Y U T L W K G R N T Y
O A S R Y D G E A F A U V L
K C R P O G I R R L C M Q L
W A U R I T O T A I L B F O
T S K Q O O O O C A Y A Z U
W O M B A T K P O H J T B Q
B E K N J P B N P V G E J Y
```

27

Cities and Towns of Australia

ADELAIDE

BRISBANE

BUDERIM

CANBERRA

DARWIN

HORNSBY

IPSWICH

KINGSTON

LISMORE

MANLY

MELBOURNE

MILTON

NEWCASTLE

NOOSA

OAKLEIGH

PENRITH

PERTH

RICHMOND

SANDY BAY

SOUTH YARA

SOUTHPORT

SYDNEY

TOWNSVILLE

WOLLONGONG

```
K I N G S T O N F Y V F S O
H M E L B O U R N E L E U M
M I L T O N U A N A S N U N
M R L W V E R T R O E A A E
D E I Y Y R R A H W O B D M
N D V O E A Y O C P N S U C
O U S B O H B A M H O I A C
M B N E T Y S Y B S N R O H
H A W U U T S L D J I B T D
C W O L L O N G O N G L A A
I S T E D I A L E D A R B U
R P E N R I T H C I W S P I
O P L U O A K L E I G H L E
P E R T H B Y E N D Y S N H
```

29

Birds of North America

BLUE JAY

CONDOR

CORMORANT

DOVE

DUCK

EAGLE

EGRET

FALCON

GOOSE

HAWK

HERON

HUMMINGBIRD

LOON

MALLARD

PELICAN

PETREL

PHEASANT

PIGEON

PUFFIN

QUAIL

ROBIN

SANDPIPER

SPARROW

WOODPECKER

```
P  W  T  K  J  I  N  O  I  I  X  M  M  D
M  U  O  K  T  Y  T  O  E  L  G  A  E  Z
L  J  F  O  C  P  S  N  O  C  L  A  F  M
W  L  A  F  D  U  A  P  A  L  T  E  Z  R
Y  R  E  P  I  P  D  N  A  S  N  K  D  W
O  B  F  R  C  N  E  R  M  R  A  J  H  T
O  O  R  F  T  O  D  C  E  G  R  E  T  V
R  O  B  I  N  E  P  R  K  S  O  O  H  E
Z  Q  L  Q  N  G  P  M  Y  E  M  O  W  P
T  H  U  M  M  I  N  G  B  I  R  D  S  O
G  L  E  A  K  P  R  O  D  N  O  C  R  E
S  Y  J  W  I  Z  W  Y  R  V  C  B  O  W
A  N  A  C  I  L  E  P  E  E  V  C  Q  O
N  H  Y  C  B  U  E  V  D  P  H  I  S  N
```

Mexico

ACAPULCO

ALAMEDA

AZTECS

BAJA

BEACHES

CANCUN

CHIHUAHUA

COZUMEL

ENCHILADAS

GUADALAJARA

GULF

MARIACHI

MAYA

OAXACA

PESO

PYRAMIDS

SCUBA

SONORA

SPANISH

TACOS

TORTILLA

TOSTADAS

UXMAL

YUCATAN

```
T G C P E S O N O R A B I X
O P T P Y D O U N R C K Y S
Q J O W U S X C A C A X A O
A R R O C M S J A P P U D S
M F T B A J A Y Y T U S E P
G A I L T L D R U F L H X A
C U L S A D A L I H C N E N
N H L D N M T M E A O E B I
P A A F I U S J E M C G J S
O U E D M M O B S D U H R H
G H S V A Z T E C S A Z I G
H I O U Y H V X U I R J O Z
I H X X A Y G T B M F T A C
S C A N C U N P A G R D Q Z
```

33

Capitals of Europe

AMSTERDAM	MOSCOW
ATHENS	OSLO
BELGRADE	PARIS
BONN	PRAGUE
BRATISLAVA	ROME
BRUSSELS	SOFIA
BUCHAREST	STOCKHOLM
BUDAPEST	VADUZ
HELSINKI	VIENNA
LONDON	VILNIUS
MADRID	WARSAW
MINSK	ZAGREB

```
U Z I K S N I M R X D Q R D
Z I V M Q Y O M V B A G O M
F A I F O S B D I R D A M S
E B M Q A S U I N L I V E Z
M P R S T O C K H O L M N A
E L I U T K H O W W L I N G
H Y N K S E A S W E E I T R
A T H E N S R I I J U O S E
N N W D L I E D A R G L E B
N B R A T I S L A V A S P O
E Y O O R N T L S M R P A N
I S D O L S O N E A P U D N
V A D U Z I A C O H I T U I
N V S K N T W W D S P G B W
```

35

Scandinavia

ARCTIC

BERGEN

COPENHAGEN

DANISH

DENMARK

EUROPE

FINLAND

FINNS

FJORDS

GLACIERS

HELSINKI

KRONE

MARKKA

NORDIC

NORSE

NORTH

NORWAY

OSLO

REINDEER

SKIING

STOCKHOLM

SWEDEN

TIVOLI

VIKINGS

Z A M N E G G Q E C U X U C
Q M T F J N O R T H B G J A
I L O V I T O S L O C O J A
W Y A I N N D R N O R W A Y
N H K M S G N I K I V K B E
E S R O N X A S I O K E S I
C I T C R A L K N R R R F F
S N C O P E N H A G E N J B
U A J G C I I M E I U O Z Q
D D Z O S K F N C X R R S U
F U A L W R H L D D O D O R
V R E F I E A O S E P I W E
S H G B P G V H L F E C K U
E Z W S W E D E N M A R K P

37

Spain

BARCELONA	MARBELLA
BEACH	OLIVES
BULLS	PAELLA
CATALAN	PAMPLONA
CORDOBA	PICASSO
EL PRADO	SAN ISIDRO
FLAMENCO	SEVILLA
GAZPACHO	SPANISH
GRANADA	TAPAS
IBERIA	TOLEDO
MADRID	VACATION
MALAGA	VALENCIA

```
P S X D B W F S O J B O P M
A F L S P W T L B S D P N A
E M H L E Y I A A A D G L L
L F A K U V B N R M S R S A
L A I R E B I P C W E A C G
A B M S B S L L E K Q N G A
A O A O I E N A L A T A C N
Y D D D S Y L V O A Z D H O
O R R E R S N L N P R A T L
H O I L M V A C A T I O N P
P C D O D A I C N E L A V M
P T A T L D H S I N A P S A
A D E E F O Z T A P A S I P
F I Y O B U A R Z X X W P I
```

39

Switzerland

ALPS

BANKS

BASEL

BERN

CHEESE

CHOCOLATE

EMMENTALER

FONDUE

FRANC

FRENCH

GENEVA

GERMAN

GRUYERE

HIKING

IBEX

ITALIAN

LUCERNE

MATTERHORN

REPUBLIC

SKIING

SNOW

ST MORITZ

SWISS

ZURICH

```
N M Q S W I S S Y G Y D A R
Y S O O X R Y X K Q C P V Z
V K T O Z G N I K I H M E L
N N A M R E G E L G I M N K
V A I A O P U B R E M N E G
Y B D T V R U D T E S Q G S
M J W T I P I A N Y Y A G O
M L P E E T L T L O A U B Z
T F C R H O A U Z P F N R K
Y R P H C L C L C Z S T M G
O A U O E E H C I R U Z W W
Z N H R R E L C F A U O J L
I C F N I H S F R E N C H H
N R E B Z I B E X S X E G B
```

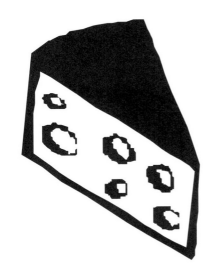

France

ARTS

BREAD

BRIE

BURGUNDY

CAFE

CHEESE

CROISSANT

EIFFEL

EUROPE

FOOD

FRANC

FRENCH

LOUVRE

LYON

MARSEILLE

MONA LISA

PAINTING

PARIS

PROVENCE

RENOIR

RIVIERA

TRAVEL

VACATION

VERSAILLES

B V P X B I P R O V E N C E
J L M M J M A L M M P X P Q
M R N A U T I O A J O A I C
E B U R G U N D Y F R B H U
H Y U S X A T A R I U E P G
Z I S E L L I A S R E V C N
Q T F I O O N E C S O N G O
R A S L U C G C E E I R B I
F A P L V Z A B A R Q O U T
H C N E R F J R I V I E R A
D O O F E J X O T H T A R C
B E Y F T H N P G S V W F A
U N L I H E C F J E W V N V
O D A E R B S T L A B W D N

Greece

AEGEAN
ATHENS
BAKLAVA
BEACHES
CRETE
CYCLADES
EASTER
EUROPE
FETA
GREEK
GYROS
HELLAS

ISLANDS
MYKONOS
OLIVES
OLYMPICS
PATRAS
PIRAEUS
PLATO
SHEEP
SOCRATES
SPANAKOPITA
SPARTA
ZEUS

```
Q D F S B X A L F R A V U G
E U R O P E S H E E P M F P
N J Q Y G A A J W T A E C E
D E S E T A R C O S T G R S
G A A S C S Y T H A R R F S
Y N Y U N C O P A E A E U B
R X D E L I S N Z T S E A C
O S H A C P L D O V Z K E H
S T D R N M Q T N K L I E R
A E E I Y Y A M U A Y L R C
S T V P R L Q P V Z L M P W
E A T I P O K A N A P S E M
T O Y R L M B K S H M Y I Z
Y H D F M O Z E U G H F N R
```

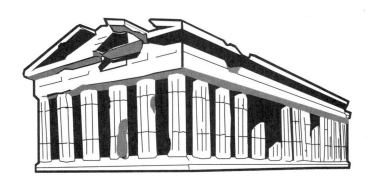

45

Italy

AMALFI	NAPLES
ANTIPASTO	OLIVE OIL
BOOT	PASTA
CALAMARI	PIZZA
CAPRI	RENAISSANCE
COLISEUM	ROME
FLORENCE	SALAMI
GELATO	SARDINIA
GONDOLA	SICILY
ITALIAN	TUSCANY
MICHELANGELO	UMBRIA
MILAN	VENICE

```
V N I U O A T F V U W M P K
G H T N M X S U Q P U M W A
U E A A B B A X S E I I A M
W L L S O L R W S C R Z Q I
T F I A O T B I H N A X Z L
I Z A D T H L E A A M N U A
E C N E R O L F I S A O Y N
S O A V C A F N S S L E B H
G A P S N I I G C I A B J W
I B L G P D N K V A C W N I
X Y E A R O M E B N P I N V
Z L S A M R O I V E O R L U
O T S A P I T N A R X U I Y
A Z J D L N U I I X D S D H
```

Capitals of States and Provinces

ALBANY

ANNAPOLIS

ATLANTA

AUGUSTA

BOSTON

CONCORD

DENVER

EDMONTON

FRANKFORT

HALIFAX

HARTFORD

HONOLULU

JACKSON

JUNEAU

LANSING

LINCOLN

MONTGOMERY

PHOENIX

PIERRE

QUEBEC

SACRAMENTO

SPRINGFIELD

TOPEKA

TORONTO

```
E  Y  H  C  E  B  E  U  Q  V  J  E  Y  C
R  D  A  V  J  A  C  K  S  O  N  W  N  L
R  E  R  I  W  O  I  V  B  Z  F  F  A  I
E  N  T  M  N  Y  L  H  P  O  R  N  B  N
I  V  F  C  O  M  O  J  M  A  S  R  L  C
P  E  O  A  N  N  U  X  N  I  A  T  A  O
D  R  R  T  O  N  T  K  N  N  C  O  O  L
D  Z  D  L  E  I  F  G  N  I  R  P  S  N
X  L  U  A  H  O  O  A  O  B  A  E  H  I
D  L  U  N  R  L  P  V  W  M  M  K  U  I
U  N  O  T  N  O  M  D  E  H  E  A  X  M
J  S  H  A  L  I  F  A  X  Y  N  R  V  B
H  E  X  I  N  E  O  H  P  E  T  H  Y  P
A  T  S  U  G  U  A  O  T  N  O  R  O  T
```

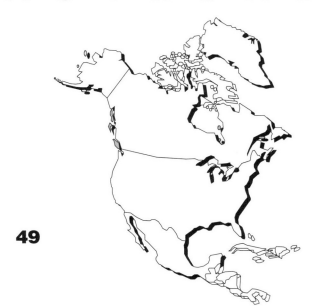

49

Caribbean and the West Indies

ANGUILLA

ANTIGUA

ARUBA

BAHAMAS

BARBADOS

BARBUDA

BONAIRE

CAYMANS

CUBA

CURACAO

DOMINICA

GUADELOUPE

HAITI

JAMAICA

MARTINIQUE

MONTSERRAT

PUERTO RICO

SABA

ST LUCIA

ST MAARTIN

ST THOMAS

TOBAGO

TORTOLA

TRINIDAD

```
A C I A M A J I G V I O D H
O U J S O D A B R A B F A T
F R G Q A O A L W O X I O S
I A V I W M G B L C T M E T
D C J C T I O A M I A P M L
C A Y M A N S H B R U O Y U
A O D Y A I A A T O N G S C
L N H I D C H I L T T S N I
O G R J N A N E S R S A B A
T E K B M I D E U E P V R T
R E O A Q A R K R U D U R R
O C S U U R L T F P B P Z C
T Z E G A D U B R A B U C T
Q O S T M A A R T I N K V I
```

51

Egypt

ABU SIMBEL

AFRICA

ALEXANDRIA

ARABIC

ASWAN

CAIRO

DELTA

DESERT

HATSHEPSUT

HERMOPOLIS

HIEROGLYPHICS

HIGH DAM

LUXOR

MOSLEM

MUMMY

NILE

PHARAOH

PYRAMID

RAMSES

RED SEA

SINAI

SPHINX

TEMPLES

TUTANKHAMUN

```
H A T S H E P S U T N I L E
S I N A I X X V K X Q J W V
E L E B M I S U B A M N Q G
H O A R A H P E C I B A R A
D M A O O S I I L Z D W H T
T E E L E G R G H P U S V P
Y L S D E F L T H O M A C D
A S D E A X X Y V D I E I E
P O E L R U A R P Z A M T X
Z M R T U T A N K H A M U N
Q U I A S M I R D R I A H I
C M E Z S H X F Y R Z C A H
T M H E R M O P O L I S S P
Y Y S P C L U X O R I A C S
```

53

Languages

ARABIC	JAPANESE
ENGLISH	LATIN
ESKIMO	LITHUANIAN
FINNISH	MANDARIN
FLEMISH	POLISH
FRENCH	RUSSIAN
GAELIC	SPANISH
GERMAN	SWAHILI
GREEK	SWEDISH
HAWAIIAN	TAGALOG
HEBREW	UKRAINIAN
ITALIAN	YIDDISH

```
P  O  L  I  S  H  P  D  F  V  N  Q  L  W
G  G  N  A  I  S  S  U  R  U  T  I  G  E
Z  F  R  Q  T  T  M  J  F  M  T  N  F  R
N  P  V  E  N  I  A  I  V  H  A  R  I  B
A  Q  O  S  E  I  N  L  U  I  F  D  N  E
M  C  M  H  U  K  R  A  I  N  I  A  N  H
R  M  I  E  S  E  N  A  P  A  J  H  I  O
E  E  K  B  W  I  W  S  D  B  N  W  S  Y
G  T  S  C  A  A  L  F  S  N  S  P  H  P
G  A  E  N  H  R  H  G  O  L  A  G  A  T
A  D  E  C  I  U  A  O  N  N  L  M  C  K
A  T  H  L  L  S  Y  W  I  E  S  S  Z  U
F  L  E  M  I  S  H  S  I  D  E  W  S  M
N  F  R  E  N  C  H  S  I  D  D  I  Y  N
```

Informatie

55

Languages of Asia

BALINESE

BENGALI

BUGIS

BURMESE

CANTONESE

GUJARATI

HAKKA

HINDI

JAPANESE

KANNADA

KHMER

KOREAN

MALAY

MANDARIN

MARATHI

ORIYA

PUNJABI

SINDHI

TAGALOG

TAMIL

TELUGU

URDU

VIETNAMESE

ZHUANG

```
P U N J A B I M P U N C
H A F U G U L E T R B E
Z I H T A R A M E D U N
W A N U M R R S U G A
J B D D H E V K E Y I E
G A E A I S S S M M R
O U K N E E I A E H O L
L K J P G N L M N K G K
A Y R A O A A I T D Z O
G A B T R P L K E L H R
A L N U M A F I I I U I
T A G X B J T H V M A Y
C M A N D A R I N A N A
P B G T U W X A V T G K
```

57

Fish

ANCHOVY

BARBEL

BASS

BLOWFISH

BREAM

CARP

CATFISH

DARTER

DORADO

FLOUNDER

FLUKE

GOLDFISH

GROUPER

HERRING

MARLIN

PERCH

PIKE

PIRANHA

SALMON

SNAPPER

STEELHEAD

STURGEON

TROUT

TUNA

```
O K O P E R C H V E C B X W
H W K S L Y K S K A K Y X P
R E I T E D P I X N E P K B
S R R U A K P F F U J L L D
M S P R A C O D F T U O R T
A B T G I T G L R X W F D C
E E R E D N U O L F P H S H
R S E O E K G G I G L N S L
B N N E L Q S R N N I H M
P O R A N C H O V Y F L G Q
M M Y D P Q U E T T B R N R
B L I Q E P I R A N H A E D
B A R B E L E C F D X M S O
I S Y R L D O R A D O U R S
```

59

Wild West

BANDIT	OKLAHOMA
BLACKSMITH	OUTLAW
CALIFORNIA	ROBBERY
CAVALRY	SADDLE
DODGE CITY	SALOON
DYNAMITE	SHERIFF
GOLD MINE	SPURS
HOLDUP	STAGECOACH
HOLSTER	TEXAS
HORSES	TRAINS
MARSHALS	UTAH
NEW MEXICO	WYOMING

```
S R U P S S N E L D D A S D
N E R B B W Y O M I N G E K
O E D G L M A R S H A L S J
O U T L A W H K E I G A R C
L N X C C E C U N B M U O A
A E Z P K G A R T H B H H V
S W E S S I O K L A H O M A
N M B T M F C L Q Y H L R L
I E Y T I C E G D O D D Q R
A X M L T M G S L M Y U W Y
R I A W H D A S B A I P T Z
T C S A X E T N T I D N A B
X O N X S E S S Y W F P E J
U S H E R I F F F P D L K Z M
```

61

Oceania

AITUTAKI

AUSTRALIA

CAROLINE

COOK ISLANDS

FIJI

GUAM

KIRIBATI

MARIANAS

MARSHALL

MICRONESIA

NAURU

NEW CALEDONIA

NEW ZEALAND

NIUE

PALAU

PALIKIR

PITCAIRN

POLYNESIA

RAROTONGA

SAMOA

TAHITI

TONGA

TUVALU

VANUATU

```
I C P U E V L V H T O W M Z
T F A I A D J W A A H T A I
A D I R T R Z G B N E U G D
B U N J O C M M P J U V N T
I A O A I L A R T S U A O U
R R D T L R I I T P N L T P
I I E A S A S N R N A U O U
K K L H N H E E E N N L R M
V I A I R W N Z O G Y Z A C
P L C T Y E O B W N A U R U
L A W I U E R A E E G W H V
Z P E I F T C S W F N C L S
S D N A L S I K O O C H X X
V S A M O A M A R I A N A S
```

63

Basketball Players

ARCHIBALD

BARKLEY

BARRY

BAYLOR

BIRD

CHAMBERLAIN

CHEEKS

EWING

GILMORE

HAWKINS

HAYES

JOHNSON

JORDAN

LUCAS

MALONE

OLAJUWAN

PETTIT

REED

ROBERTSON

ROBINSON

RUSSELL

STOCKTON

THURMOND

WEST

```
T P U L L E S S U R E E D V
V I N N M H N E O U Y E H M
O S T O D L A B I H C R A E
Q S J T S I I C N H H O Y Y
N T G K E N O L A M E M E Y
W O W C S P H M W T E L S U
T J S O U C B O U E K I P X
H L N T Y E J H J R S G C X
U F J S R O L Y A B E T Y Q
R E I L R E Q B L W G D S L
M W A D A M B A O Q K R P U
O I A Y B K U O S R I I N C
N N Q Y K E C V R P O B N A
D G E Q U L G U E M L D Q S
```

65
```

```

Baseball

BALL

BASES

BATTER

BUNT

CATCHER

COACH

CURVE

DIAMOND

DOUBLE

FASTBALL

FIELD

HOME RUN

MANAGER

PITCHER

POP UP

SINGLE

SLIDE

STADIUM

STANDINGS

STEAL

STRIKE

SWING

TRIPLE

WORLD SERIES

```
E K I R T S I N G L E M U L
Q I C K P S N A F N L L W H
S T E A L E N S Y B B A C T
P T P I T C H E R B U A B E
H X D S T C D I A M O N D V
D E B T T F H R T C D P T L
E L M A N A G E R L P E N E
U D E D T S N S R E L U P E
R E B I P T V D V P R R L V
V W N U F B E L I E G F L G
S C P M A A S R M N V P F D
I O A S W L T O I T G R I V
P Z E M I L H W T G Z S U J
E S G R I L S D O P R X X C
```

67

Basketball

BALL	LOSER
BLOCK	PLAYOFFS
CENTER	POINTS
COACH	PROFESSIONAL
DUNK	QUARTER
FORWARD	SCORE
FOUL	SHOOTER
FREE THROW	SHOT
GAME	TEAM
GUARD	TIPPED
HALFTIME	WINNER
JUMP	WNBA

```
S P R O F E S S I O N A L Z
H H M V R A B L O C K H M I
W L O S E R K D E P P I T T
P R J O E Y I N H T K S L J
Y L E M T U T A U C K L F X
T Y A T H E W D D D A U P F
Y G O Y R A R I Y B O O F G
Q H W D O A L O N Y I F C S
S P D Y W F U F C N T N Y X
T V A R Y E F Q T S E B N V
S C O F A D Q S I I A R W Z
L F I P M U J X V J M B Q Q
H N P Y V T G Y V K R E N S
K N O V U L X X C A Q N C W
```

69

Bowling

ALLEY	OPEN
APPROACH	PERFECT
ARCH	PINS
BALL RETURN	PINSETTER
BOWLER	SCORE
BRUNSWICK	SHOES
COMPETITION	SPARE
CURVE	SPIN
GLOVE	SPLIT
GUTTER	STRIKE
LANES	TOWEL
LOSER	WINNER

```
P P S A B Q P V L O G S S M
O I C P T N R G C Z A H K C
U N O I T I T E P M O C X G
D S R Z N C L Q T E O R C T
Z E E U E R A P S T P A U E
Q T K F T I I Q S W U C R R
S T R I K E B E V O L G V Y
W E H C A O R P P A F C E G
P R L S W D P L N V W L Y O
E T Y L T O W E L I L D K C
R X E E M M S O N A P L J X
T R K C I W S N U R B S Q Z
Q M H S J E E P R B P Z U M
F H Y X R R I O O B M Y A B
```

71

Football

CENTER

CLIP

COACHES

DEFENSE

FIELD GOAL

FOOTBALL

GUARD

HALFTIME

HELMET

HUDDLE

KICKER

PADS

PASS

PENALTY

PUNTER

QUARTERBACK

REFEREE

RUSH

SAFETY

SCORE

TACKLE

TEAM

TOUCHDOWN

VICTORY

```
C G G C K I M O Y H N H D X
W K C C S A F E T Y S E V H
A Q C L I P O O L S F U S Y
H K N A O J U M A E T X R V
B U Y O B C R P N H P O I D
E M D G H R T S E C U C G E
X Z S D A P E M P A T C L O
M K O L L A B T O O F K G D
K W E E F E L H R C C L R P
N I S I T W E Y E A Y A W W
H L C F I L R E T N U P J G
Z A F K M Y Q J N G W Q P A
X T U E E R E F E R O C S D
T N T Y W R Y G C N Q U R X
```

73

Golf

BALL

BIRDIE

BUNKER

CADDIE

CART

COUNTRY CLUB

DRIVER

EAGLE

FAIRWAY

GREEN

HAZARD

NICKLAUS

PALMER

PULL

PUTTER

RANGE

SAND TRAP

SCORE

SLICE

TOURNAMENT

TREE

TREVINO

WEDGE

WINNER

```
P W N Y L C F K Z T Y B I V
N U G F T K A N P V T I K W
G S L I C E I D R I B M I B
E D E L U C R N D U Z W B C
F U G Z K I W R L I E I B F
X P N L V A A C G D E A R Y
A W A E T Z Y J G F L Z Q M
B U R R A R R E M L A P G X
S A A H T N E M A N R U O T
Y C R N W D K V S G M T U L
W N U S R E N N I W L T T T
U O T W E M U A C N E E R G
C Y E B A D B Z S C O R E Q
S S I K Y W V S F C E R E Q
```

Martial Arts

AIKIDO

CAPOEIRA

CHULAS

HAPKIDO

IAIDO

JU JITSU

JUDO

KARATE

KENDO

KICKBOXING

KRAV MAGA

KUNG FU

KYUDO

MUAY THAI

NAGINATA

NINJUTSU

SAVATE

SHINTAIDO

SILAT

SOMBO

TAE KWON DO

TAI CHI CHUAN

TAIDO

TANG SOO DO

```
M S W X J S R S A V A T E O
W U A H U S O M B O A A D D
D K A R J J Z B K N G I B I
P Y T Y I P G O G A K C P A
P W A X T E C S M I T H K I
U T N Q S H O V A A M I O J
W N I A U O A P L Q C C D T
S H G L D R O I A K P H I S
E T A O K B S K B C M U A I
T S N P O D N O W K E A T G
A G P D K W X J J Y J N N J
R X N R U I U S T U J N I N
A E Y G N M D M D D L F H X
K U N G F U P O L O Q V S X
```

77

Emmy Awards

ACTOR

ACTRESS

ANIMATED

COVERAGE

CULTURAL

DESIGNER

DIRECTOR

DRAMA

EDITOR

GRAPHICS

HAIRSTYLING

HISTORICAL

INTERVIEW

LIGHTING

MAKEUP

MUSIC

NEWS

PERFORMER

SONG

SOUND

SPORTS

TALK SHOW

VIDEO

WRITER

```
O E D I V L I G H T I N G E
E G K N A C T R E S S T N W
F A N E U I N A O N J J O E
D R M I Q O F P S T W M S E
I E T A L K S H O W C C L O
R V S L R Y S I R S X A Z X
E O C I Q D T C E A C R S H
C C U U G C J S M I T R I W
T A L T I N T E R V I E W R
O Q T S P E E O O I P F K I
R Q U Q T W T R F N A B O T
G M R U Y S P O R T S H X E
T G A N I M A T E D I T O R
Q I L H Z A I I P U E K A M
```

79

Famous Actors

AFFLECK	CRUISE
ALLEN	CRYSTAL
AUTRY	DREYFUSS
BELUSHI	EASTWOOD
BOGART	FONDA
BRANDO	GABLE
CAGE	GIBSON
CHAPLIN	HOFFMAN
CONNERY	HOPKINS
COOPER	KEATON
COSBY	PACINO
COSTNER	REDFORD

```
Z  O  E  G  N  F  Y  Z  K  N  D  M  H  F
Z  F  W  H  D  B  H  J  C  R  U  I  S  E
A  K  F  H  O  D  J  B  E  L  U  S  H  I
K  E  Q  G  O  F  R  Y  L  A  L  Q  W  W
E  U  A  O  W  P  F  O  F  O  N  D  A  M
A  R  C  J  T  U  K  M  F  I  K  A  Q  B
T  A  R  H  S  U  H  I  A  D  R  J  P  I
O  M  Y  S  A  H  C  O  N  N  E  R  Y  E
N  P  S  R  E  P  O  O  C  S  N  R  C  D
Y  R  T  U  A  G  L  N  J  O  T  J  S  G
H  Q  A  L  P  A  C  I  N  O  S  B  I  G
X  E  L  L  X  B  R  A  N  D  O  B  U  Z
U  E  S  B  H  L  D  Z  G  O  C  P  Y  E
N  M  Z  Z  S  E  O  O  L  E  B  F  C  B
```

Famous Actresses

ANDREWS

BARDOT

BASSETT

BERGMAN

BULLOCK

CLOSE

COLLINS

CRAWFORD

DAVIS

DENCH

DIETRICH

FIELD

FOSTER

GARBO

GARLAND

GRABLE

HARLOW

HAWN

HEPBURN

KELLY

LEIGH

ROBERTS

ROSSELLINI

STANWYCK

E C P G R A B L E H G I E L
A H X H A U A H A A L I Q R
J X T L L R H R Y W I Q O R
H F P L D B L C N N I B B X
U E O C A O J A I N E A R W
O C H S W Y M L N R R S A H
K R C N T G L Y T D T S G C
J A N D R E W S O A Q E K N
V W I E S U R T N V Y T I E
G F B S O R B W Z I I T F D
A O O O D L Y P X S L W O J
S R C L L C F I E L D L U V
S D K C K E L L Y H O E O D
J P V Q L R Z M P Z M R R C

83

Skiing

ASPEN

AUSTRIA

BOOTS

CHAIRLIFT

COLORADO

DOWNHILL

GOGGLES

LAKE TAHOE

LODGE

MOUNTAIN

PATROL

POLES

POWDER

RACE

RESORT

SKIS

SLALOM

SLOPE

SNOW

SWITZERLAND

TRAIL

UTAH

VAIL

VERMONT

```
I  H  D  J  E  I  F  P  A  K  Q  T  H  F
Q  N  T  M  N  J  A  P  D  L  R  J  W  D
S  Q  N  F  Q  E  U  R  O  O  E  K  E  G
D  E  W  T  I  V  S  R  S  W  J  G  C  A
M  B  L  J  R  L  T  E  J  H  D  V  A  R
L  O  G  O  D  A  R  O  L  O  C  E  R  R
L  D  M  J  P  K  I  I  L  G  O  R  R  Z
S  T  O  O  B  E  A  L  A  W  G  M  F  M
W  M  U  W  L  T  I  S  N  H  D  O  S  S
W  V  N  K  N  A  I  I  P  D  C  N  G  Z
N  H  T  U  V  H  L  K  K  E  O  T  Z  S
P  Q  A  H  H  O  I  S  V  W  N  C  V  L
S  W  I  T  Z  E  R  L  A  N  D  X  L  F
L  H  N  K  U  K  Q  S  L  O  P  E  V  Z
```

85

Tennis

BACKHAND

CHANG

COURT

DOUBLES

FOREHAND

HINGIS

LINES

LOVE

PLAY

RACQUET

SAMPRAS

SCORE

SELES

SERVE

SHORTS

SINGLES

SLICE

TENNIS BALL

TOURNAMENT

UMPIRE

VOLLEY

WHITES

WINNER

YELLOW

```
R Z L K B I S U F A E K S D
A S T L J A U A O O R F I T
Y V G N A H C Q R Y I N N A
A E R L Y B B K E P P E G M
O O L I N E S T H L M S L Y
E C I L S H E I A A U A E Y
A R Y H O U L G N Y N L S Z
T H O R Q V B R D N L D I R
Y C T C H V U L E O E I G E
T S A T S O O R W N K T N A
A R E L T V D G X C N N I K
C N U L E V R E S E T I H W
P H X O E H S G I N I C W U
L V V S C S H U W N F T A H
```

87

Track and Field

ATHLETE

COACH

DECATHLON

DISCUS

DISTANCE

FAST

HAMMER

INDOOR

JAVELIN

JUMP

MARATHON

METERS

MILE

OLYMPICS

OUTDOOR

RECORD

RELAY

SHOT PUT

SNEAKERS

SPEED

SPRINT

TRACK

TRAINER

TRIATHLON

Z K C A R T L Y D A B S Q K
P S Q U M O M N L P P T G H
H L P U I N O R N R U O K Z
E C T E L P O D I P Q N K G
M J A V E L I N T S A F D H
L C N O W D T O W U B R N I
Y Q A F C I H H N N O O P H
Y W T K L S Y T M C L K A S
N A H C Y T R A E H Y M A J
N O L H T A I R T P M U J A
J C E E I N V A E E P R H W
F C T N R C C M R I I F H Z
S R E K A E N S S U C S I D
H R O O D N I U Q J S J D K

89

Artist

ACRYLIC	PALETTE
ARTIST	PAPER
BRUSH	PASTEL
CANVAS	PORTFOLIO
CHISELS	PRINT
COLOR	SCULPTURE
EASEL	SHADE
FRESCO	SKETCH
MIXING	STYLE
MURAL	SUBJECT
MUSEUM	TEXTURE
PAINT	WATER

```
U  P  A  P  E  R  U  T  P  L  U  C  S  W
S  P  C  F  E  E  D  O  A  J  X  Y  R  F
H  A  L  F  K  T  R  S  I  W  L  B  R  P
A  C  Y  B  R  T  L  U  N  E  J  M  I  I
D  R  W  W  F  E  E  T  N  I  R  P  G
E  Y  T  O  S  L  S  S  S  X  U  H  N  A
Q  L  L  I  J  A  A  C  I  A  E  C  L  W
T  I  H  Y  S  P  V  N  O  R  E  T  A  W
O  C  E  S  I  T  G  N  K  D  T  E  X  Q
I  I  E  U  U  V  Y  F  A  N  V  K  K  R
L  Q  I  J  I  R  O  L  O  C  V  S  U  Q
L  S  S  P  B  J  B  K  E  V  X  T  H  M
D  M  U  E  S  U  M  U  R  A  L  K  C  V
W  F  G  D  L  O  S  T  O  M  J  R  Y  K
```

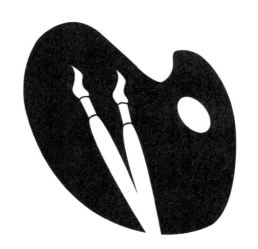

Beach

BATHING SUIT	SHARK
BIKINI	SKIING
BLANKET	SUNBATHING
FLORIDA	SUNNY
HAWAII	SUNTAN
HEAT	SURFING
JAMAICA	SWIM
LIFEGUARD	TOWEL
LOTION	UMBRELLA
OCEAN	VOLLEYBALL
SAILING	WATER
SAND	WAVES

```
C M X Y E E R S S I S F B S
N T V N T E U U D U T Y N V
A O I N B L A N K E T M R I
H W R U L L A B Y E L L O V
J E J S S J A M A I C A S
D L A L B G Q T S N Q R K X
F L O T I O N H A W A I I M
U L Q R K F S I G W I P Y G
J T O S I U E N H N A M S N
M A C R N Q I G G T M T K I
O W E T I L K I U V A B E F
O X A W I D S E V A W B E R
B N N A K B A L L E R B M U
Q B S H A R K D X W O D P S
```

93

Camp

BOAT	HAMBURGER
BUGS	HOT DOG
BUNKS	LAKE
CABIN	LETTERS
CAMPFIRE	OVERNIGHT
CAMPING	ROWBOATS
CANOE	SUMMER
COUNSELOR	SWIM
CRAFTS	TENNIS
DUFFEL	TENTS
FLASHLIGHT	TRUNK
FRIENDS	WOODS

```
I C C H J E D N C M W U Y R
D O A C S U M M E R T C Z O
K U V M E P T Z Q H A N B M
K N F E P Q E G Q M K F O I
G S U F R I N Y P J K G T W
D E H S E N N F R I E N D S
F L A S H L I G H T S M R K
Q O M Q T R S G U B J E W G
R R B R E A J E H C T S O G
X R U R E P O K A T E V O F
I N R S K N U B E S N D D B
K S G G A R I L W Q T A S Q
M Q E C L N G A O O S S I T
X I R T I Y E I H Z R X W F
```

95

Classic Books

AENEID

ANIMAL FARM

ANTIGONE

BELOVED

BEOWULF

BILLY BUDD

CANDIDE

CLOWN

CRITO

DEERSLAYER

DON JUAN

DRACULA

EMMA

FLATLAND

GREAT GATSBY

GUIDE

IDIOT

ILIAD

IVANHOE

JANE EYRE

MOBY DICK

ODYSSEY

REPUBLIC

WALDEN

```
N  G  U  T  E  S  W  T  Y  E  R  J  K  I
A  N  R  D  B  A  X  B  C  O  W  X  E  L
C  A  I  E  L  Q  E  A  L  R  K  D  W  I
N  U  Y  D  A  L  E  N  O  G  I  T  N  A
G  J  E  K  O  T  H  I  W  D  B  T  I  D
I  N  A  V  N  E  G  M  N  I  S  N  O  A
D  O  E  N  R  E  Y  A  L  S  R  E  E  D
I  D  O  U  E  K  C  L  T  F  T  N  O  N
O  D  Y  S  S  E  Y  F  D  S  E  T  H  A
T  Y  K  T  V  B  Y  A  Q  I  B  D  N  L
C  I  L  B  U  P  E  R  D  V  P  Y  A  T
K  C  I  D  Y  B  O  M  E  M  M  A  V  A
G  W  D  R  A  C  U  L  A  N  T  F  I  L
H  H  L  Q  H  V  K  B  E  O  W  U  L  F
```

97

Collectibles

ANIMATION

ANTIQUES

AUTOGRAPHS

BOOKS

BOTTLES

CARDS

CARS

CLOTHING

COINS

COMICS

DOLLS

FOSSILS

FURNITURE

GEMS

GLASS

JEWELRY

LAMPS

MILITARIA

PINS

RADIOS

RECORDS

STAMPS

TOYS

TRAINS

```
J M H M J S T R A I N S N O
S N I P L K A O S G E X U Y
O K C L X D W P Y P D S B A
Q C O M I C S R D S H R X W
W D B O T T L E S P M A L I
Y V S U B E A E A P S C I M
C K Y C W F U R N I T U R E
T B Q E L Q G C I C A R D S
Q I J X I O Q Q M A M X L D
G F L T T B T X A X P I S R
E L N U L W L H T I S K L O
M A A L N O L D I S N I O C
S F H S E V Q D O N W L I E
Z O Z Z S G O F N M G V J R
```

99

Evening News

ANCHOR	LOCATION
CABLE	NATIONAL
CAMERA	NETWORK
COVERAGE	NEWS
ENTERTAINMENT	REPORTER
FILE	SOUND
INTERNATIONAL	SPORTS
INTERVIEW	STATION
LATE	TAPE
LIGHTS	TELEVISION
LIVE	VIDEO
LOCAL	WEATHER

```
P Z P Z I L B K A U N W T Q
M L C G C N R T N N S E A B
S T A T I O N B C A P N V N
X L B N W I V Y H T O Z O G
S M L T O S N E O L R I R P
T N E M N I A T R E T N E Q
H N T X D V T P E A S B T I
G T U A R E M A C R G Z R S
I O T V P L Q O N C V E O W
L P L I V E L I F R H I P I
P A C D X T O H V T E M E B
Y B C E R A H B A F Q T R W
D N U O S L N E W S N G N L
N X U V L O W S H X Q C N I
```

Exercise

AEROBICS

BICEPS

CARDIO

CLUB

CRUNCH

FITNESS

HEALTH

JOGGING

LIFT

MUSCLES

PUSHUPS

RUNNING

SITUPS

SORE

STRENGTH

STRETCH

SWIM

TREADMILL

TRICEPS

WALK

WEIGHTS

WORKOUT

YOGA

```
E  C  S  T  X  S  N  M  C  W  X  P  G  U
H  C  N  U  R  C  S  I  J  P  R  X  S  H
X  S  T  H  G  I  E  W  B  I  C  E  P  S
H  I  K  K  H  B  S  S  O  J  G  W  K  P
X  T  B  S  T  O  T  P  N  R  G  V  Z  E
F  U  A  Y  S  R  R  X  U  Y  K  H  R  C
S  P  E  D  E  E  E  N  J  H  E  O  V  I
G  S  I  T  V  A  N  A  Y  E  S  M  U  R
Q  N  C  L  W  I  G  T  D  I  B  U  N  T
D  H  I  A  N  K  T  O  I  M  E  S  P  X
U  F  L  G  R  U  H  Q  Y  F  I  C  C  P
T  K  U  J  G  D  X  P  H  E  A  L  T  H
C  Z  J  H  S  O  I  J  N  J  U  E  L  C
K  P  S  Y  E  Z  J  O  E  B  F  S  J  E
```

Fishing

ANGLER

BAIT

BOAT

CASTING

CHARTER

FISHERMAN

FLIES

FLYROD

GUIDE

HARPOON

HOOKS

LAKES

LEADER

LINE

LURES

OCEAN

REEL

RIVER

SALTWATER

TACKLE

TRAWLING

TROLLING

TROUT

WORMS

```
P S F L J K H P R E L G N A
N H W B B U W N E T N O R P
A T X O Q Y W A V R O C C H
E A A J R Q F Q I P N H A L
U T U C Q M I Z R K A J S K
Q W L A K E S A V R E C T S
O Q M N R L H W T M C R I F
X L Z R T L E E R Y O F N P
G U I D E T R A W L I N G I
I R B F N D M F L Y R O D T
O E Y L K B A I T M E B U W
D S G I L I N E S K O O H K
S J B E I G R W L I R C J T
I T G S A L T W A T E R Q A
```

105

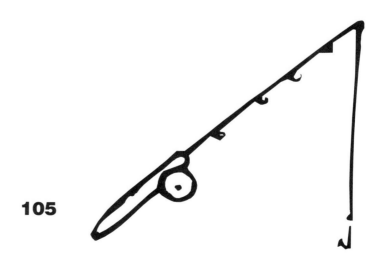

Music

ALTERNATIVE	JAZZ
BLUES	LATIN
CHANTING	METAL
CLASSICAL	MUSICAL
COUNTRY	OPERA
DANCEHALL	PUNK
DISCO	REGGAE
FOLK	ROCK
GOSPEL	SOUL
HIP HOP	SPANISH
HOUSE	SWING
INDUSTRIAL	TECHNO

```
G C F I D X M L R W B R Y C
M S W I N G K A Z L V R K E
U B F S P D N C T A L E E T
F Y U L Z M U I I T V G Z W
B T G J D E U S T I M G G F
O E B S D T Q S T N Z A X N
K C T Z Z A J A I R A E O U
U H Z F B L N L M C I H Q J
Z N H S R R O C K P A A C Q
G O S P E L O C E O U L L E
N Y R T N U O C P H K N S V
F O L K H O L E S P A U K H
Q A K N P S R B S I O L S W
L X B S P A N I S H D Y L K
```

107

Photography

ALBUM	LENSE
BLACK	PAPER
CAMERA	PHOTO
COLOR	PICTURE
DARKROOM	PORTRAIT
DEVELOP	PRINTS
EXPOSURE	PROOFS
FILM	SAY CHEESE
FLASH	SLIDES
IMAGE	SOLUTION
KODAK	WHITE
LANDSCAPE	ZOOM

```
H Y N P E M P C G D E T U X
S T N I R P D O A Z I G W X
A D D Y U K A Y L M H G Y W
L H P E S A Y C H E E S E L
F S F O O R P F S T V R S I
M L S E P B T O I D O E A O
R I Y G X U L H R L N P D Z
R D I A E U W A O T M A C E
A E L M T S J C C V R P L R
E S Q I Z Z N G M K C A F F
O T O H P B O E R U T C I P
Z N O B Z S X O L Y B J O T
J C V Q Y U O V M T F L M H
A C S W V M P V D K O D A K
```

109

Slumber Party

CANDY

DANCING

FLASHLIGHT

FRIENDS

GAMES

HOUSE

JOKES

LATE

LAUGH

MAKEUP

MOVIES

MUSIC

NIGHT

PAJAMAS

PILLOWS

PIZZA

POPCORN

PRESENTS

PRETZELS

SLEEP

SLEEPING BAG

STORIES

TELEVISION

TOOTHBRUSH

```
P I F O H C K G T F F O J P
T G C G C X O G L I Y L M G
A A U A I J N A S W H U J P
F A N B J I S T N E S E R P
L D D G C H T S H I I E C A
Y Z J N L Q O W C G T V H J
S J A I X H R O S Z I G O A
H D G P X P I L E U P N U M
L H N E U R E L K W O P S A
T E L E V I S I O N P F E S
M T K L I C F P J U C J X E
L A H S U R B H T O O T T M
M L W D J M F Y H Y R K C A
A I P I Z Z A A F J N W Y G
```

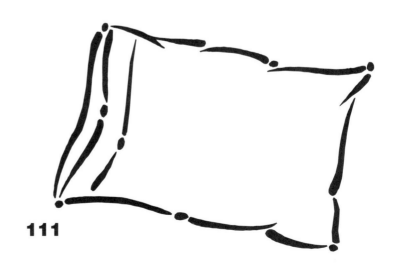

111

That's Sharp

BARB

BAYONET

DAGGER

FISHHOOK

FORK

GLASS

HARPOON

HATCHET

ICEPICK

JAVELIN

KNIFE

LANCE

MACHETE

NAIL

NEEDLE

SCISSORS

SCREW

SKEWER

SPEAR

SPIKE

SPUR

STAPLE

SWORD

THUMBTACK

```
W  N  C  M  P  K  D  R  O  F  U  R  N  P
A  Q  F  B  S  N  E  U  V  V  O  S  D  R
S  V  B  N  P  I  H  P  N  F  T  R  M  V
U  P  T  B  E  F  I  S  H  H  O  O  K  D
W  X  I  T  A  E  K  R  U  W  G  S  P  A
H  K  C  K  R  R  D  M  S  R  F  S  N  B
S  K  E  W  E  R  B  L  M  G  T  I  S  Z
M  I  P  H  A  T  C  H  E  T  J  C  N  H
Z  A  I  B  A  Y  O  N  E  T  R  S  H  Y
I  G  C  C  I  R  C  Q  L  E  T  W  W  S
A  L  K  H  I  A  P  A  W  A  O  C  D  L
D  A  G  G  E  R  K  O  P  M  N  A  I  L
L  S  S  J  O  T  Z  L  O  M  X  C  Y  Z
X  S  C  J  A  V  E  L  I  N  Y  B  E  S
```

113

Tools

CROWBAR

DRILL

GRINDER

GRIP

HACKSAW

HAMMER

HATCHET

HOOK

JIGSAW

MALLET

PICKAX

PLANE

PLIERS

ROUTER

SANDER

SCISSORS

SCREWDRIVER

SCROLL SAW

SHEARS

SHOVEL

SPADE

TROWEL

WIRECUTTER

WRENCH

```
G X U C U R S H E A R S U M
U O K E E E A X A I E P H S
O G P T U C P S M L F C C
M K U S C T E L L A M R N R
D O O H R U I N G O E E R E
R U E O S C D E N L H O R W
I T W V H E G R L K A J W D
L E E E S R O S S I C S W R
L I Q L I I A P I C K A X I
W Y C N F W A B T Q S N P V
T A D Z O D S P W G A D M E
T E O K E J U Z I O W E K R
R X W B W L H J X R R R Y J
V Y C F F H A P V R G C Q I
```

115

Dance

BALLET

BALLROOM

BELLY

BREAK DANCE

CLOGGING

CONTRA

FLAMENCO

FOLK

HULA

JITTERBUG

KRAKOWIAK

KUCHIPUDI

MERENGUE

OBEREK

ODISSI

POLKA

SALSA

SAMBA

SQUARE

SWING

SWORD

TANGO

WALTZ

ZYDECO

D Z A O E C Y O Z Y P C Z R
U L B A M T L B L O L F C L
O B E R E K X O A A K L O P
J I T T E R B U G L B A E E
W D K N R A U A G G L M M B
B U V O A K K N L U I E A K
Y P X C U O I D T L R N T S
E I C R Q W C X A E R C G N
K H I S S I D O N N K O G F
H C I A W A P G G L C X O I
V U L L O K U B O E H E W M
J K L S R E R F D N S H S E
M V Q A D N A Y Y Q E U I O
K H R M Y X Z T L A W X Y A

117

Fabric

ACETATE

BROADLOOM

BURLAP

CASHMERE

CHAMBRAY

CORDUROY

COTTON

CRINOLINE

DENIM

FELT

FLANNEL

FLEECE

GAUZE

KNITWEAR

LINEN

NYLON

PAISLEY

POLYESTER

RAYON

SATIN

SILK

SUEDE

VELVET

WOOL

```
I  T  F  U  T  E  V  L  E  V  S  V  Y  R
S  M  G  O  P  K  R  A  E  W  T  I  N  K
N  O  L  Y  N  F  W  N  M  N  K  C  K  L
Y  O  M  G  T  J  I  G  M  B  N  H  C  O
Y  L  T  P  A  L  G  A  C  E  T  A  T  E
P  D  N  T  O  X  K  U  N  W  S  M  L  C
U  A  R  N  O  L  O  Z  Q  H  G  B  O  F
F  O  I  S  I  C  Y  E  M  E  Y  R  O  Y
H  R  A  S  U  E  D  E  M  W  D  A  W  F
C  B  R  N  L  C  R  I  S  U  J  Y  H  G
D  G  L  I  N  E  N  K  R  T  F  O  J  E
G  V  U  T  K  E  Y  O  K  G  E  N  W  O
I  I  P  A  D  L  Y  R  P  A  L  R  U  B
B  G  Q  S  Z  F  F  L  N  A  T  J  L  Q
```

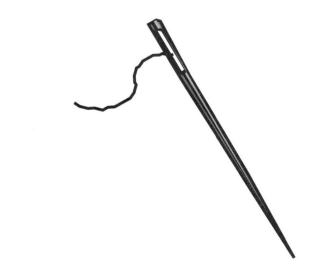

119

Green

APPLE

AVOCADO

CELERY

CLOTHING

COLLARDS

CUCUMBER

GRASS

HONEYDEW

KIWI

LAWNS

LEAVES

LETTUCE

LIME

MARTIAN

MEADOW

MINT

MOLD

MONEY

PARSLEY

PEPPER

PINE TREE

SALAD

SPINACH

UNRIPE

```
V  I  G  T  I  I  W  H  Q  C  F  F  R  E
B  R  R  S  N  W  A  L  M  S  L  M  U  L
A  N  U  W  O  I  P  E  P  P  E  R  S  O
D  B  N  D  E  K  D  L  B  I  Y  D  H  G
L  Y  A  M  B  C  K  Q  E  N  R  H  Y  R
O  E  I  I  G  S  U  O  D  A  C  O  V  A
M  L  T  N  N  N  A  C  L  C  V  N  P  S
F  S  R  T  F  C  M  L  U  H  P  E  N  S
N  R  A  J  U  Q  O  O  A  M  Y  Y  S  P
H  A  M  V  S  C  L  T  N  D  B  D  L  V
E  P  I  R  N  U  E  H  C  E  L  E  R  Y
K  P  J  O  P  H  V  I  U  U  Y  W  R  W
P  L  E  E  R  T  E  N  I  P  W  O  G  H
C  E  O  D  P  V  S  G  M  O  L  E  N  K
```

121

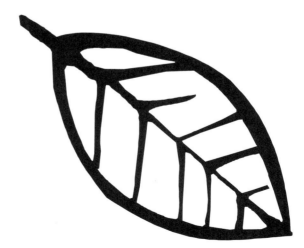

Red

BLOOD

CANDY APPLE

CHERRY

CLIFFORD

COLOR

DEVIL

FIREBALL

FIRETRUCK

HAIR

HEART

LADY BUG

LAVA

LIPSTICK

PEPPER

PUNCH

REDHEAD

ROSE

ROUGE

RUBY

SANTA

STOP

STRAWBERRY

TOMATO

VALENTINE

Y B T G Y M R R W D G A L S
R L R O U G E L E T C T A A
R H C N U P I V X D R N V Z
E S T O P P I T O I C A I T
H L T E S L Z O I R L S E Y
C A P T T J L M L E I O W H
K O I P R B P A N D F D O J
S C F R A V D T B H F P B W
K Y I N W Y I O C E O C K W
G F B P B N D O L A R Z U H
P K E U E D L N D D D I X T
Z U G E R O S E A F T U F M
Z J F I R E T R U C K P M I
R L A Y Y I U K F M B Q W Q

123

Halloween

BLACK CAT	NIGHT
BROOM	OCTOBER
CANDY	ORANGE
CHOCOLATE	PARTY
CORN	PUMPKIN
COSTUME	SCARY
FALL	SHAVING CREAM
FRIGHT	SPIDER WEB
GHOST	SPOOKY
GOBLINS	TREAT
HAUNTED	TRICK
HOLIDAY	WITCH

```
S Z S L Y E T P Z Y G T D F
A H T R Q K G H D I R H T S
N P A R G U O N X E F S B B
P C C V I L A O A Z V Q R I
S Y K H I C S T P R J O H F
E F C D O N K K E S O B R H
C O A Y I C G B Y M E C L M
V Y L L N R O C T W V O S A
M Y B Q L T C L R O I S H P
D O H T C H H E A E C T L C
G T S O H G D G P T A U C Z
P U M P K I N P I B E M I H
U H K G P R H A U N T E D Z
S R S S F F N W S P G W O Y
```

125

Thanksgiving

APPLES

AUTUMN

CIDER

COLUMBUS

CRANBERRY

DINNER

DRUMSTICK

FALL

FAMILY

FEAST

HARVEST

HOLIDAY

MAYFLOWER

NOVEMBER

PIES

PILGRIM

SETTLERS

STUFFING

THANKS

TRAVEL

TURKEY

VACATION

WISHBONE

YAMS

```
O C D V W G C Z L H C C Z J
S R Q A E K E I F X Y H T Q
Y F Y C C Y L B D C O S V O
R A P A H O E T S E V R A H
Y U D T M U L K U C R E W T
R K C I T S M U R D E L I O
R E W O L F Y A M U Y T S C
U H B N A O N L A B T T H T
J E P M F B H S P P U E B H
G D I R E N N I D F P S O A
Q L T R A V E L F A L L N N
Y U R P S S O I V Y L Z E K
D Y W W T W N N M U T U A S
R R M I R G L I P A A R T D
```

127

Christmas

BELLS

CANDY CANE

CELEBRATION

DECEMBER

EGGNOG

ELVES

FAMILY

FRUITCAKE

GIFTS

HOLIDAY

LIGHTS

NORTH POLE

PRESENTS

REINDEER

RUDOLPH

SANTA

SHOPPING

SLED

SNOW

SNOWMAN

STOCKING

TREE

WINTER

WRAPPING

```
G O N G G E L W J F V X B C
H Z X X S L L N A M W O N S
S C Y A D I L O H A F D U W
L B N A U G N I P P O H S R
R T D F I H J T C H X I E A
A F R U I T C A K E T L S P
S Q Y E V S N R R S V R T P
Q F L E I D X B X E E H O I
S L I I Y N E E S B T R C N
I U M C A H D L M E U N K G
I N A Z S T N E S E R P I S
W N F Q S C C C E I G F N W
E E R S B E L L S R T A G N
H P L O D U R C V S T Q Y P
```

129

Valentine's Day

ARROW

BE MINE

BOYFRIEND

CANDY

CARD

CHOCOLATE

CUPID

DANCING

DARLING

DATE

DINNER

FEBRUARY

FLOWERS

GIFTS

GIRLFRIEND

HALLMARK

HOLIDAY

JEWELRY

LOVE

NECKLACE

RING

ROMANCE

ROSE

SWEETHEART

```
H O K R W R B Y Y O K Y I N
Q R Q N G Q D J R R V R O I
W R P D C A A Y A D I L O H
T O I D N F R M U C W E F E
A M R C W E L G R H M W L Y
E A I R L L I I B O B E G J
C N X M A U N R E C O J E E
G C I H K G O F O Y C S D
L E O M S R E W O L F O T W
Y O S W E E T H E A R T F S
D D V N D B T B W T I I I Y
Z P N E C K L A C E E N G D
N I X A S R Q S D B N N N O
D I P U C J U T I K D Q E F
```

131

Fourth of July

AMERICA	HOLIDAY
ANTHEM	HOT DOG
BANNER	NATIONALISM
BARBEQUE	PARTY
BEACH	PATRIOT
BLUE	PICNIC
CELEBRATE	POOL
FIREWORKS	SPARKLER
FLAG	STAR
FLIES	STRIPES
FREEDOM	SUMMER
HAMBURGER	WHITE

```
D  S  S  V  Y  S  T  R  I  P  E  S  N  Q
R  E  N  A  M  T  M  F  E  U  O  Q  F  W
S  I  R  J  B  O  H  K  Q  N  O  O  H  S
W  L  W  E  P  N  D  E  J  A  N  I  L  N
N  F  A  T  G  I  B  E  I  M  T  A  C  Z
H  C  I  A  P  R  C  T  E  E  T  K  B  G
H  R  H  R  A  M  U  N  O  R  I  O  Y  N
I  A  O  B  E  P  E  B  I  I  F  T  O  W
B  T  L  E  W  W  C  H  M  C  R  L  H  R
M  S  I  L  A  N  O  I  T  A  N  T  A  Z
E  F  D  E  Y  T  B  R  P  N  H  F  A  G
A  N  A  C  D  R  E  L  K  R  A  P  S  P
A  Y  Y  O  R  E  M  M  U  S  M  B  U  Q
G  V  G  Z  J  P  R  M  Y  E  B  D  E  L
```

133

Anybody Thirsty?

APPLE

CIDER

COCOA

COFFEE

COLA

EGGNOG

FLOAT

GRAPEFRUIT

ICED TEA

JUICE

LEMONADE

LIMEADE

MILK

MILK SHAKE

NECTAR

ORANGE

PUNCH

ROOT BEER

SELTZER

SMOOTHIE

SODA

SOFT DRINK

TONIC

WATER

```
O Y A L S R Y R N A L J Z S
I Z O O E L P P A G N U M T
M F C C K S M O O T H I E R
F Q O T N W K H R R C C D F
U L C M I L K S H A K E A B
A D O S R U E R R L N E N K
X E F A D L R E B T O O R
D G F G T Q Y F I D Q H M B
I N E Z F E D A E M I L E P
J A E I O G G C J P W C L S
E R E Q S G I I R M A Y L O
T O Y P U N C H F A T R X E
G I O B O O I E B N E K G E
I O Z T E G P O F P R R Y C
```

135

Barbecue

CELEBRATION

CHARCOAL

CHICKEN

CHOPS

COLESLAW

FIRE

FISH

GAMES

GRILL

HAMBURGER

HOT DOG

ICE TEA

LAWN

LEMONADE

MARINADE

PARTY

PEOPLE

RIBS

SAUCE

SMOKE

SOCCER

SPICES

SPICY

STEAK

```
U L G Q N Z Q H I B S L P R
L C Q T P T X S P L M H E B
G J E U Y X I E E E A C Y J
I O D L L M V Q K M C W J M
F Z A W E U S J B O A U N F
L F N W Y B C U S N M G A S
C C I T I S R O N A O S S S
X H R R N G J A L D P E F R
Z A A G E N A E T E C I C G
P T M R K W U O O I S H T T
Z S P I C Y H P P H O L Z L
M E D L I O L S M P R N A O
F N L L H E A M S T E A K W
M E V S C J C L D E L Z Q Z
```

137

Bread

BAGEL

BAKING

BRIOCHE

BUTTERMILK

CARAWAY

CIABATTA

CORN

CROISSANT

FLAT

FLOUR

FOCACCIA

FRENCH

LANDBROT

LAVASH

OVEN

PITA

POTATO

RAISIN

ROLL

SEMOLINA

SODA

SOURDOUGH

WHEAT

WHITE

T C P C P P L N T I M E D T
A B R I O C H E R H A R R D
O H U C T H A T G L X B R A
T Q G T A A A T T A B A I C
E A O U T K Z Y N M B K D W
F X N D O E Y R A I S I N W
X H E T R D R F S W F N I W
N G V U B M R M S X A G X C
M Y O F D E H U I D J R T Z
O L J Z N S E M O L I N A L
F O I C A X T S R S K R L C
E V H V L A I C C A C O F G
M T A E H W H O A Z R C T T
J L T W R X W H M W L P C T

139

Breakfast

BACON

BAGEL

BISCUIT

BREAD

BUTTER

CEREAL

COFFEE

DANISH

DOUGHNUT

EGGS

FLAPJACK

FRUIT

GRANOLA

GRITS

JELLY

MILK

MORNING

MUFFIN

OATMEAL

PANCAKES

SAUSAGE

SYRUP

TOAST

WAFFLE

```
E  W  D  K  B  S  A  L  S  D  M  A  W  A
C  J  L  T  A  A  E  G  T  X  U  A  C  G
R  N  T  I  C  M  G  K  H  F  F  M  O  H
S  Q  O  U  O  E  P  E  A  F  F  Z  S  T
E  H  P  C  N  S  R  Z  L  C  I  I  L  K
T  O  A  S  T  H  U  E  O  X  N  H  C  P
R  K  L  I  M  I  G  F  A  A  A  A  E  R
P  Z  R  B  J  A  F  U  D  L  J  F  P  W
T  G  A  B  S  E  G  V  O  P  U  R  Y  S
P  T  K  U  E  D  L  N  A  D  X  T  N  B
F  O  A  T  M  E  A  L  Z  N  I  T  S  M
S  S  M  T  Y  R  F  E  Y  U  T  M  U  N
U  R  U  E  G  N  I  N  R  O  M  I  Y  T
L  X  L  R  Q  N  O  F  N  B  M  L  X  I
```

141

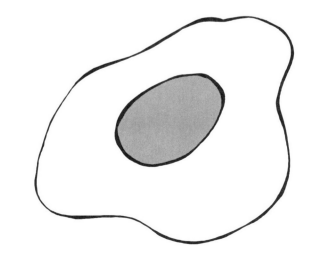

Desserts

APPLE PIE

BROWNIE

CAKE

CHEESECAKE

CHOCOLATE

COBBLER

COOKIE

CUPCAKE

DANISH

DOUGHNUT

ECLAIR

FROZEN YOGURT

FRUIT

ICE CREAM

JELLO

MACAROON

MOUSSE

PARFAIT

PASTRY

PECAN PIE

PUDDING

SHAKE

SHERBERT

SUNDAE

```
K V I I W P C O B B L E R G
X F L C R Y E P A R F A I T
H R R D E S T C O O K I E P
T U S O S C R X A W R R E A
H I H U Z H R K E N B I G S
V T O G S E J E T I P Y S T
V M I H R E N E A E W I H R
V D A N I S H Y L M J E E Y
I K K U A E A P O L Z L R Z
E Q W T L C P K C G O B B E
H Z M A C A R O O N U R E R
V V P K E K P K H C A R R B
S U N D A E K A C P U C T B
P G A D B G N I D D U P S Q
```

143

Pies

APPLE	MERINGUE
BANANA	MINCEMEAT
BERRY	PEACH
BLUEBERRY	PECAN
BOSTON	PISTACHIO
CHERRY	PIZZA
CHOCOLATE	PLUM
COCONUT	PUMPKIN
CREAM	RHUBARB
DUTCH	SHOOFLY
KEY LIME	SPINACH
LEMON	STRAWBERRY

Y Z L B F N N Z F O C Y Y C
V R H U B A R B B O S T O N
Y V R K C X H E I P M C A J
D M Y E U D U C I N O M E L
P A P Y B G A N A N A B E Z
Y E C L N W A D U E U X T F
K R O I H C A T S I P A A T
P C R M H Y R R E B E U L B
U E U E N D D Z T M F A O C
M L G Y H K H O E S P L C C
P I Z Z A C G C G P H S O C
K W W G T H N Y L F O O H S
I Q B U C I H E Q N D B C S
N U D G M D J G P L B V Y W

145

Sundaes

BANANA	ICE CREAM
BOWL	PEANUTS
BUTTERSCOTCH	SCOOP
CALORIES	SPOON
CARAMEL	SPRINKLES
CHERRY	STRAWBERRY
CHIPS	SWEET
CHOCOLATE	SYRUP
COCONUT	TREAT
COLD	VANILLA
COOKIE	WALNUTS
FUDGE	YUMMY

```
B F Q A L X K G W W F M C J
Y U M M Y W M J B G H H S R
F D T I Y M O L T E E W S B
M G S T R A W B E R R Y A O
P E E K E E K A R M R N L X
G D L Q T R J Y L U A R V S
S W K Q A C S V P N M R V U
T E N N L E C C A H U B A C
U I I B O C O C O N U T H C
N K R R C I O P R T I M S D
A O P N O O P S R V C L D T
E O S R H L L E F V A H L R
P C P U C V A D E K M G S A
H B A H D T F C H I P S S W
```

147

Diner Food

BACON

CEREAL

CHILI

COFFEE

FRENCH TOAST

FRIED EGGS

FRIES

GRAVY

HAMBURGER

JELLO

MEATLOAF

OATMEAL

OMELETTE

PANCAKES

PORK CHOP

POT PIE

SALAD

SANDWICH

SAUSAGE

SOUP

TOAST

TUNA

TURKEY

WAFFLES

```
P R S T F Y R U O B V J U K
R Z W E R A P T O H E Q E L
D S J R K C O M E L E T T E
A F Y P O A H L L W F C A U
L X T F T A C O T U R K E Y
A R F M Y F K N B A I H B L
S E E I C E R E A L E A Y H
E A A E N S O I D P S M L C
L B U P O T P I E A Y B C I
F Q Z S C M N C I D F U G W
F S T S A O T H C N E R F D
A R H O B G L I Z B A G D N
W A N U T L E L M V C E G A
B G Q P Y C C I Y Y O R M S
```

149

Fruit

APPLE

BANANA

CANTALOUPE

CHERRY

CRANBERRY

GRAPE

GRAPEFRUIT

GUAVA

KIWI

LEMON

LIME

MANGO

MELON

NECTARINE

ORANGE

PAPAYA

PEACH

PEAR

PLUM

RASPBERRY

STRAWBERRY

TANGELO

TANGERINE

TOMATO

```
E G W N X J B G S U P A A W
A R S R T B Z G T V L Y N A
E A L E A K Q H M O R A E P
D P W P N S K O C R M P L Q
R E U C G V P L E A V A U G
A F I O E P E B D N E P T V
K R N M L B W O E Y N P Q O
Q U O U O A G C D R I L E I
I I M R R N T V P R R E S U
T T C T A A Q N K E E Y W R
N L S M R N S O A H G S E D
F I W I K A G M S C N F J L
D M N O Y R R E B N A R C M
B E R D S N O L E M T M D F
```

151

Herbs

ANISE

BALM

BASIL

BAY LEAF

CAMOMILE

CARAWAY

CHERVIL

CILANTRO

CLOVER

CORIANDER

DILL

FENNEL

GINSENG

LICORICE

MINT

MUSTARD

OREGANO

PARSLEY

ROSEMARY

SAGE

SAVORY

SORREL

TARRAGON

THYME

```
M D P Y E L S R A P X M G J
I I T R R Q Y R D T K X J I
Y L I O R A A R O F Y G Y E
O L E V W O M R L W N L C Q
O D I A F Y E E L E M I N T
X R R S A G E D S S R V A D
N A T U A J C N B O A R R C
C T V N T B I A C W R E O F
G S O H A G Y I M A V H M S
W U Y L A L L R G O F C G E
V M M O E O I O L J M Y S P
E R S A S Z N C O E F I E K
S I F Y I R S F E N N E L H
I A H Q L X W C U A K U E E
```

153

Nuts

ACORN

ALMOND

BETEL

BLACK

BRAZIL

CANDLENUT

CASHEW

CHESTNUT

CHINQUAPIN

COCONUT

CUMARA

FILBERT

GRUGRU NUT

HAZELNUT

KOLA

LITCHI

MACADAMIA

PALM

PEANUT

PECAN

PINE

PISTACHIO

SOUARI

WALNUT

```
D  K  K  Q  I  X  G  X  S  S  K  F  A  I
N  A  Y  C  V  B  T  V  Z  X  O  T  I  P
O  I  H  C  A  T  S  I  P  V  L  R  E  S
M  M  P  F  I  L  B  E  R  T  A  C  A  I
L  A  T  A  T  T  B  N  F  U  A  X  R  Y
A  D  S  U  U  Q  T  I  O  N  M  O  A  K
P  A  J  N  N  Q  T  S  D  T  X  T  M  T
L  C  L  V  U  L  N  L  L  S  W  U  U  O
J  A  C  O  R  N  E  I  Q  E  P  N  C  P
W  M  G  P  G  N  Z  Z  H  H  O  A  L  D
W  G  O  B  U  A  D  S  A  C  R  E  G  U
R  P  Z  T  R  C  A  V  O  H  T  P  J  H
G  N  B  B  G  C  H  C  X  E  N  I  P  N
D  Z  M  Z  J  D  O  D  B  K  A  W  L  N
```

155

Vegetables

ARTICHOKE

ASPARAGUS

BEAN

BEET

BROCCOLI

CABBAGE

CARROT

CAULIFLOWER

CELERY

CHIVE

CORN

CUCUMBER

EGGPLANT

KALE

LETTUCE

MUSHROOM

ONION

PEPPER

RADISH

SCALLION

SPINACH

SQUASH

TURNIP

ZUCCHINI

```
J  C  P  I  N  R  U  T  R  K  D  F  F  K
Z  U  A  N  O  I  N  O  I  L  L  A  C  S
S  C  S  U  G  A  R  A  P  S  A  K  G  M
C  Q  G  I  L  O  C  C  O  R  B  C  Y  R
H  I  U  P  K  I  A  E  T  S  O  U  E  P
H  Q  G  A  O  N  F  I  G  Q  Z  C  V  G
P  G  L  S  S  I  C  L  D  A  A  U  I  O
E  E  M  U  S  H  R  O  O  M  B  M  H  W
P  K  N  R  O  C  Q  W  P  W  I  B  C  C
P  T  Z  K  V  C  W  T  Y  X  E  E  A  F
E  L  E  T  T  U  C  E  E  A  L  R  N  C
R  C  G  C  M  Z  R  D  N  E  R  J  I  F
J  A  Q  H  S  I  D  A  R  O  B  M  P  G
P  P  E  K  T  U  X  Y  T  O  P  A  S  N
```

157

What's on the Table?

ASHTRAY

BILL

BOWL

BREAD

BUTTER

CANDLE

CUPS

ELBOWS

FORK

GLASS

KNIFE

MENU

NAPKIN

PAPER

PEPPER

PLACEMAT

PLATE

SALT

SAUCER

SCRATCHES

SPOON

SUGAR

TABLECLOTH

WATER

```
J X L Z S I J N K X D Y N F
X R G K R O F O M E N U T D
P W M R N Z W T B O Q E P B
V C S K I I R M O A T A H T
A D V N P E F P W A H T D C
A F T N P R S E L B O W S L
K D S A L T C P L L I B Y J
E G P P A I E P C R D Y F H
V L Z K C Y R E C U A S W C
B A D I E O L R R R E G H U
N S Y N M B U T T E R M U P
O S C R A T C H E S B W S S
G G V T T C S N P V T T J J
I Z V E W A T E R Y U I C F
```

159

In the Bathroom

BATH

BRUSH

CABINET

CONDITIONER

DEODORANT

DRAIN

DRYER

FAUCET

HAIR DRYER

LOTION

MEDICINE

MIRROR

RAZOR

ROBE

SHAMPOO

SHOWER

SINK

SOAP

TILES

TISSUES

TOILET

TOOTHPASTE

TOWEL

WASHCLOTH

toot

C A W X F F Z O E M B N R Z
G O B M G D T N D A U E P M
Z A N C A B I N E T Y A I R
F O S D L C R R O R E M T H
V P R Z I E R T D B I E Y J
A G A D W T I R O R I H N R
H T E O A S I R R W A O T D
D M H T S A H O A I E I V K
R S T U H P R Z N T L L N U
F Y E I C H S A T E C U A F
Y S L F L T N R S J R E T M
N I I A O O P M A H S U R B
C N O I T O L S Z P U L K B
C K T T H T A B T K B K E E

161

In the Bedroom

ALARM	MATTRESS
BLANKET	MIRROR
BOOKS	NIGHTGOWN
CARPET	NIGHTSTAND
CHAIR	PAJAMAS
CLOSET	PILLOW
CLOTHING	QUILT
CURTAINS	RADIO
DRAWER	SHEETS
DRESSER	TELEVISION
LAMP	TISSUES
LINENS	WINDOW

```
N K R N Z T X B D G F G M Z
W W Q V W D T M I R R O R I
V S O S N I A T R U C W X W
S Y N G E T S E U S S I T I
T V J I T R T L C H A I R N
E T T R G H J E S E U C G D
E J E H B H G V K R A N S O
H S Y P T D T I E N I R K W
S P R M R E S S N H A M O M
P A J A M A S I T J R L O K
Z E W L D E C O J A L S B Q
Z E F P R I L N L I N E N S
R O M D Z C O A P C I D C U
R W S K A E I T L I U Q M L
```

163

Get Dressed

BATHROBE

BLOUSE

BOOTS

BOXERS

CARDIGAN

COAT

DRESS

GLOVES

HATS

JACKET

JEANS

MITTENS

OVERALLS

PANTS

SCARF

SHIRT

SHOES

SKIRT

SLIPPERS

SNEAKERS

SOCKS

SWEATER

SWEATSHIRT

UNIFORM

```
K  J  F  T  B  W  C  T  N  Z  S  G  O  Z
G  M  A  W  A  S  B  F  H  U  Y  L  N  E
M  B  S  K  C  O  S  P  O  S  S  O  G  S
U  P  D  W  V  J  C  R  L  W  Z  V  N  N
E  A  H  I  E  N  B  L  E  H  J  E  M  E
J  N  U  A  U  A  A  A  X  P  T  S  R  A
W  T  N  K  T  R  T  G  P  T  P  M  A  K
B  S  I  U  E  S  H  E  I  O  N  I  P  E
O  L  F  V  H  F  R  M  R  D  F  L  L  R
O  F  O  I  L  F  O  D  S  D  R  E  S  S
T  M  R  U  U  H  B  T  E  K  C  A  J  O
S  T  M  A  S  R  E  X  O  B  I  Z  C  Q
M  P  H  G  C  E  G  V  H  F  E  R  B  N
P  F  Z  C  P  S  B  Y  S  U  N  N  T  M
```

165

Gems

AGATE

ALEXANDRITE

AMETHYST

BERYL

BRILLIANT

CITRINE

CORAL

DEMANTOID

DIAMOND

EMERALD

GARNET

GIRASOL

JACINTH

JADE

JASPER

KUNZITE

MORGANITE

ONYX

OPAL

PERIDOT

RUBY

TOPAZ

TOURMALINE

TURQUOISE

```
D  G  G  H  U  K  Z  W  O  A  B  U  O  F
Z  J  J  E  J  A  U  O  Q  R  W  Q  M
C  A  G  M  P  A  O  N  P  D  J  X  T  N
L  C  B  O  F  E  S  A  Z  A  O  X  S  W
C  I  T  R  I  N  E  P  D  I  L  E  Y  I
C  N  E  G  I  I  A  E  E  Z  T  M  H  P
D  T  H  A  U  L  M  G  A  R  N  E  T  Y
N  H  O  N  M  A  L  G  A  L  Y  R  E  B
O  S  I  I  N  M  I  I  X  T  H  A  M  U
M  O  E  T  I  R  D  N  A  X  E  L  A  R
A  N  O  E  A  U  G  W  D  N  Y  D  G  D
I  I  E  S  I  O  U  Q  R  U  T  N  E  R
D  F  O  R  U  T  O  D  I  R  E  P  O  X
R  L  A  R  O  C  C  M  E  F  V  A  T  R
```

167

In the Kitchen

BEATERS	KNIFE
BLENDER	MICROWAVE
BOWL	OVEN
COFFEE MAKER	PANS
DETERGENT	POTS
DISHES	REFRIGERATOR
DISHWASHER	SINK
FORK	SKILLET
FREEZER	SPATULA
FRIDGE	SPOON
GARBAGE	STOVE
ICE MAKER	TOASTER

```
D E T E R G E N T X H Y S D
R O T A R E G I R F E R F N
E E Y W S A H T E X E D N P
K P G S R F D S K T F I X B
A K W B T K R R A P M S T I
M S A K N H O E M W P H E B
E G D I R F B I E K H E L L
E V S S D R C C C Z D S L E
F T O P G R K N I F E W I N
F O E T O A S T E R W R K D
O X P W S O A L U T A P S E
C M A Z Y Z N N W K P F G R
T V N G Y R S T C O V E N J
E W S T O P V V F E B Q D F
```

169

It's Cold

ALASKA

ANTARCTICA

ARCTIC

CHILL

DECEMBER

DRAFT

FEBRUARY

FREEZER

FROST

FROZEN

GLACIER

ICE CREAM

ICICLE

JANUARY

MOUNTAIN

NORTH POLE

POPSICLE

SHIVER

SIBERIA

SKIING

SNOW

SNOWCONE

WIND

WINTER

S F E B R U A R Y M W W B T
J H R L W J D E O M K E S A
X A I O O I P U F E N L I S
C K N V S P N P A N E C B K
H S L U E T H D O O E I I
Y A N T A R C T I C A C R I
S L O I M R R G R W P I I N
Q A N K I E Y E F O S S A G
C F S Z T B A R P N N F R D
O H R N B M E S Y S D J R C
O I I O R E I C A L G A H G
W W U L Z C A H L X F Z E A
E P P E L E Y M O T Z T J Z
Q K R E T D N F D I W K V B

171

It's Hot

AUGUST	HOT TUB
CANDLE	INDIA
CAYENNE	IRON
COALS	JULY
COCOA	LAVA
COFFEE	MEXICO
DESERT	OVEN
EQUATOR	RADIATOR
FIRE	SAUNA
FLAME	STOVE
GREECE	SUMMER
HEATER	VOLCANO

R A O O S J D Y Y U I E K E
A V E A F R X E S G A C H R
D G U L L F V U D R T O D S
I N D I A L M O V E N F O Y
A N V Z M M G S L E S F R O
T W O O E A E D Z C J E T T
O I G R X R N N O E A E R B
R U Q Q I A E C W M Q N S T
M B A F C H O T T U B N O T
O M C Z O A S L A O C E N I
Y Z L Y L U J T L E A Y O O
G L H R G T O X O X H A R L
K R R U K R K L A V A C W O
U G A H F H Q X L R E X D T

173

Jewelry

AMETHYST

ANKLET

BEADS

BRACELET

BROOCH

CHARMS

DESIGNER

DIAMOND

EARRINGS

EMERALDS

GEMS

GOLD

JEWELS

LOCKET

NECKLACE

PEARLS

PENDANT

PINS

PLATINUM

RING

RUBY

SILVER

TURQUOISE

WATCH

```
Z  B  D  T  U  R  S  D  A  E  B  M  T  L
N  R  C  R  E  N  G  I  S  E  D  U  B  H
R  K  O  V  G  S  N  A  P  Z  Y  N  P  T
G  O  L  D  G  P  I  M  J  M  F  I  A  E
O  I  W  O  S  B  R  O  O  C  H  T  C  L
S  P  I  P  C  Z  R  N  U  X  B  A  X  K
Q  X  E  Z  T  K  A  D  S  Q  L  L  M  N
P  X  Y  N  Z  E  E  D  E  K  R  P  E  A
I  E  J  F  D  L  L  T  C  Y  B  U  R  A
B  K  A  W  M  A  M  E  T  H  Y  S  T  N
G  N  S  R  R  X  N  L  C  C  A  W  K  P
J  E  W  E  L  S  X  T  P  A  H  R  Q  I
N  K  M  P  T  S  A  C  G  K  R  T  M  N
T  E  G  S  N  W  B  H  M  P  A  B  C  S
```

175

Clean Up

BLEACH

BROOM

BRUSH

BUCKET

CLEANSER

CLOTH

DETERGENT

DISHWASHER

DUST MOP

DUSTPAN

FILING

GARBAGE

NAPKIN

ORGANIZE

PAIL

RAKE

SCRUB

SHINE

SOAP

SPONGE

SWEEP

VACUUM

WASHCLOTH

WASHRAG

```
T  V  I  E  F  V  T  V  F  M  B  O  E  T
F  A  W  N  M  U  L  B  G  O  C  H  T  K
D  C  W  E  B  X  P  W  U  O  I  Q  A  P
W  U  A  C  N  T  N  E  G  R  E  T  E  D
T  U  S  A  G  C  V  A  E  B  C  E  U  E
S  M  H  T  O  L  C  H  S  A  W  S  N  U
R  O  R  V  P  E  S  P  G  S  T  I  G  F
M  R  A  O  P  A  O  S  Y  M  H  E  S  L
A  G  G  P  W  N  N  B  O  S  N  S  I  P
F  A  P  H  G  S  L  P  U  T  A  A  J  J
E  N  S  E  O  E  P  R  R  C  P  G  W  P
U  I  F  G  A  R  B  A  G  E  K  A  R  D
D  Z  O  C  D  A  B  R  Y  E  I  E  S  N
S  E  H  O  Z  W  F  I  L  I  N  G  T  T
```

177

In the Living Room

ARMCHAIR

CARPET

CD PLAYER

CHAIRS

CLOCK

COUCH

CURTAINS

FIREPLACE

FLOWERS

LAMP

MIRROR

PAINTINGS

PIANO

PLANTS

RADIO

RUGS

SOFA

SPEAKERS

STEREO

STOOL

TABLE

TELEVISION

VASE

VIDEO RECORDER

R H H C C A Q K N S A I U O
R E M C A R P E T F G F Q R
S G D U U X A O B G O U W D
S T E R E O O D K F F A R N
D R N T O L C N I V N J S O
S R I A H C M R A O K R R P
S J O I L D E S K I E F P A
E P M N J P E R C W P K X I
P B E S L L C L O T Y M E N
O S O A S A N L L E L B A T
Z F C L K Y F A C G D E X I
A E E A T E L E V I S I O N
J G P M I R R O R E R S V G
T N V P N D N S S P I Z E S

179

Family

AUNT	GRANDSON
BABY	HUSBAND
BROTHER	INLAWS
CHILDREN	MOMMY
COUSIN	MOTHER
DADDY	NEPHEW
DAUGHTER	NIECE
FAMILY	PARENTS
FATHER	SIBLING
GRANDCHILD	SISTER
GRANDFATHER	UNCLE
GRANDMOTHER	WIFE

```
Q  Y  J  T  U  N  C  L  E  T  L  E  K  K
P  R  M  O  B  B  I  R  F  B  N  O  N  E
G  X  E  M  R  P  R  E  T  H  G  U  A  D
E  W  D  H  O  P  L  H  C  V  D  G  A  V
R  W  I  A  T  M  S  T  N  E  R  A  P  I
E  E  Q  F  H  A  Y  O  V  A  C  Q  O  B
T  H  G  M  E  C  F  M  N  A  H  K  V  B
S  P  G  G  R  A  N  D  C  H  I  L  D  Y
I  E  L  P  M  I  S  N  N  N  L  A  N  H
S  N  I  I  S  O  S  A  E  A  D  T  A  P
D  C  L  U  N  B  W  R  T  D  R  P  B  O
F  Y  O  A  J  O  A  G  Y  L  E  G  S  G
T  C  J  V  W  S  I  B  L  I  N  G  U  D
M  D  T  D  U  S  R  T  Y  V  Z  R  H  K
```

181

Flowers

BEGONIA

BUTTERCUP

CARNATION

DAFFODIL

DAHLIA

DAISY

DANDELION

FOXTAIL

GERANIUM

JASMINE

LILAC

LILY

LOTUS

MAGNOLIA

MIMOSA

MYRTLE

OLEANDER

ORCHID

PANSY

PEONY

POPPY

ROSE

TULIP

VIOLET

```
R  B  U  C  G  Y  M  T  A  R  J  J  N  U
F  O  X  T  A  I  L  O  N  G  A  M  B  N
J  D  S  C  P  R  L  N  A  S  A  B  E  L
R  F  B  E  G  O  N  I  A  C  U  E  N  L
Y  R  W  J  E  S  L  A  T  T  U  L  I  P
T  I  D  L  R  H  P  R  T  A  R  D  M  U
W  O  I  D  A  N  D  E  L  I  O  N  S  P
N  L  H  D  N  M  R  D  Y  F  O  M  A  S
Y  G  C  Q  I  C  B  N  F  U  L  N  J  Q
Y  F  R  M  U  P  G  A  W  C  S  C  G  Q
S  P  O  P  M  M  D  E  A  Y  N  O  E  P
I  S  P  M  Y  R  T  L  E  Y  V  N  X  T
A  J  M  O  L  V  I  O  L  E  T  V  T  Y
D  W  K  I  P  L  O  T  U  S  M  A  Y  A
```

183

Garden

ANNUALS	PESTS
BASIL	PLANTING
BEETLES	ROSES
BIENNIALS	SEEDS
BLOOM	SLUG
BULBS	SNAIL
CHIVES	SOIL
FERTILIZER	SPADE
FLOWER	SPRINKLER
GREEN	TOMATO
HOSE	TROWEL
MULCH	WEEDS

```
A J B M S P Z L H L Q J B F
F S O X P D B S Z C Z U C X
A P G H L S E O H Q L O V T
G R Q I A A B E S B I U O E
B I E N N I A L S N S M M Z
Y N R Z T T A F F B A D E S
I K W G I U R P L T B I B H
N L W Q N L M O O L B N L S
D E X N G S I W W S E S O R
B R A I S E L T E E B I Z J
W Q D N T V C S R E L X Z M
Y K I F S I O G L E D A P S
B D P R E H E B S U F S G M
A K A H P C V M M K G M Y K
```

185

School Time

BACKPACK

BLACKBOARD

BOOKS

CALCULATOR

CHALK

CLASSES

COMPASS

DESKS

FRIENDS

GRADES

GYMNASIUM

HOMEWORK

LIBRARY

LUNCH

NOTEBOOK

PAPER

PENCIL

QUIZ

RULER

STUDENTS

STUDY

TEACHER

TEST

VACATION

```
C T V H K R N D H L T W C C
I L T L J E J P I E S C A B
A D A B I H O B S E D A R G
C H L S L C R T U W N L J Y
C M U I S A N M Y G O C D B
W J N W R E C E S Z I U Q S
D P C Y D T S K P Z T L B S
E X H U F O O G B S A A F V
S N T J P O I R L O C T V L
K S R X B P Q E A K A O A T
S D N E I R F P P Q V R T A
T Y T R L S S A P M O C D L
N O Q W X U C P O R V Q U J
N J A C H K R O W E M O H T
```

187

Begins with "cla..."

CLACK

CLAIM

CLAIRVOYANT

CLAMBAKE

CLAMOR

CLAMP

CLAN

CLANG

CLAPPING

CLARIFY

CLARINET

CLARITY

CLASH

CLASP

CLASSIC

CLASSIFIED

CLASSY

CLASTIC

CLATTER

CLAUSE

CLAVE

CLAVICLE

CLAW

CLAY

```
B T X T C T Q N E V A L C Q
D I N L B L W K W Q V I K Q
W X Z A C L A U S E M B F S
E M G L Y B R Y C F C K H H
D Z A J M O T M L L A Y Y F
J C Z A M I V G A K A F L T
K Z L A R Q N R V C Z I O P
F C L A S S I F I E D R M F
F C L H P N K T C A C A C D
S C X A E P S A L C L L B D
V T O T S A I D E C A C A D
B W G W L S C N X N S D X W
T O C C G H I R G R H J E X
N I Y S S A L C L A T T E R
```

189

Begins with "gra..."

GRABBED

GRACE

GRACIOUS

GRADE

GRADUAL

GRADUATE

GRAFFITI

GRAFT

GRAIL

GRAINY

GRAMMAR

GRAMOPHONE

GRANDCHILD

GRANDEUR

GRANDMA

GRANITE

GRANOLA

GRANT

GRANULAR

GRAPES

GRAPHIC

GRASP

GRASS

GRATEFUL

```
Y  B  T  V  G  R  A  T  E  F  U  L  B  X
U  N  S  N  G  R  A  N  D  M  A  Z  E  T
E  A  I  E  G  R  A  P  H  I  C  E  O  F
R  A  N  A  P  P  S  F  S  D  Q  Y  E  A
G  L  L  G  R  A  C  E  F  L  T  N  Y  R
R  A  T  O  R  G  R  A  C  I  O  U  S  G
A  U  E  G  N  R  Z  G  B  H  T  W  S  R
D  D  E  B  B  A  R  G  P  C  R  I  A  A
E  A  M  D  G  D  R  O  F  D  F  M  R  N
Y  R  U  R  N  U  M  G  W  N  M  W  G  I
E  G  A  Z  R  A  L  U  N  A  R  G  R  T
I  N  X  R  R  T  R  P  R  R  P  N  H  E
T  L  A  G  J  E  R  G  C  G  R  A  I  L
A  C  X  R  D  Y  Z  L  F  O  P  T  M  Z
```

191

Begins with "pla..."

PLACE

PLAID

PLAINLY

PLAINTIFF

PLANE

PLANET

PLANK

PLANNED

PLANT

PLANTATION

PLAQUE

PLASTER

PLASTIC

PLATE

PLATEAU

PLATINUM

PLATOON

PLATTER

PLATYPUS

PLAUSIBLE

PLAYER

PLAYFUL

PLAYOFFS

PLAZA

```
X M T D C O C F I K D G X R
W G P D A L M K P R D U E E
N Q L V R Z R L P Z G Y I O
E C A L P E A C P L A N K I
L C T M T L T L W L V Y K M
L L E T K B A S P L A Q U E
P L A S T I C I A E P N P X
Q L U L D S P P N L I N E D
P L A Y F U L L A T P G Q T
J M Q P L A N T A T I O N P
P L A I N L Y L N T A F G P
L B V N X P P L A Y O F F S
S E E Z U U L V Z J F O H F
B D J S H I F E O L J B N P
```

193

Presidents of the United States

ADAMS

BUCHANAN

BUSH

CARTER

CLEVELAND

CLINTON

EISENHOWER

FORD

GARFIELD

GRANT

HARDING

HOOVER

JACKSON

KENNEDY

LINCOLN

MADISON

MONROE

NIXON

REAGAN

ROOSEVELT

TAFT

TRUMAN

WASHINGTON

WILSON

```
Z U K E O R N O M D Z R D X
U W P I E I S E N H O W E R
A S I T D N W A S M A X O G
N N R L M L L N O S K C A J
W A T E S E E I H M Y N H Z
C N K V V O L I N C O L N A
R A X E J A N B F N I X O N
F H L S N G Q H Z R L D S R
K C N O T N I L C E A S I C
Y U F O H I E Y Y A T G D Z
A B N R D D P D T G B R A H
M N A M U R T W Y A D A M S
Q K Y L M A O I B N F N B U
R E V O O H H F S V P T U B
```

195

Trees

ACACIA

ALDER

ALMOND

APPLE

AVOCADO

BALSA

BANYAN

BEECH

BIRCH

CASHEW

CEDAR

CHESTNUT

CYPRESS

LARCH

LIVE OAK

MAGNOLIA

MAPLE

MYRTLE

OLIVE

PECAN

REDWOOD

SPRUCE

WALNUT

WILLOW

```
Q B L A R C H W O L L I W R
L X J D B A N Y A N T K C C
Z O D T N E D M C L P N H C
F V Z P K O E E A T N Q E A
G I E L P A M V C J L U S H
S E M A G N O L I A I T T C
N A C E P C A E A L N C N R
D B V U A Z Y K V B O P U I
B O R D R Y B P R I E V T B
R R O V R P M Y R T L E A L
A G Z W E H S A C E W L C W
T K W R D Z T K H I S X Y H
M A P P L E R E V A E S J Q
B I Z B A N R X X C N B M F
```

197

Constellations

ANDROMEDA	HOROLOGIUM
AQUARIUS	HYDRA
ARIES	LIBRA
CANCER	LUPUS
CARINA	LYNX
CETUS	MENSA
COLUMBA	ORION
CORVUS	PISCES
CRATER	SCORPIUS
DORADO	SERPENS
GEMINI	TAURUS
HERCULES	VIRGO

```
N E L S O L R K E F C U X N
Z F S G G A Y G A R D Y H V
S W E U R C S N E P R E S D
V Y L N I A D F X M Y P E S
O S U I P R O C S O I P C G
Z W C R O I A R K M E N S A
D U R M W N B U P O C C I O
O B E O C A M O Q S E X P G
R D H E R S U R U A T D C R
A V R I A I L S U P U L A I
D Z E A T C O R V U S R W V
O S I J E D C N R Q B S L Y
U P H O R O L O G I U M L R
Q N A R W V D T L Y Q V R Q
```

199

Measurements

BARREL

BUSHEL

CARAT

CORD

DRAM

DROP

GALLON

GRAIN

KILOGRAM

KILOMETER

LITER

MEGATON

METRIC TON

MILE

MILLIGRAM

OUNCE

PECK

PINT

POUND

QUART

STONE

TABLESPOON

TEASPOON

YARD

```
N  H  S  V  D  B  C  L  I  W  J  R  C  M
H  V  V  J  P  O  U  N  D  O  X  U  M  E
L  L  R  H  E  C  D  S  U  W  M  J  K  T
K  C  E  P  G  K  T  N  H  E  I  I  A  R
Z  L  T  R  N  C  U  T  E  L  B  E  I  I
G  R  I  J  R  E  T  E  M  O  L  I  K  C
T  D  L  O  P  A  A  M  G  E  I  W  M  T
E  A  R  G  R  S  B  R  S  T  G  C  B  O
C  I  G  A  P  A  P  H  G  R  A  I  N
X  P  C  O  Y  M  O  S  F  V  A  A  N  K
Q  I  O  I  N  O  T  A  G  E  M  U  U  P
O  N  R  P  N  O  L  L  A  G  A  P  O  Q
V  T  D  Z  N  X  M  T  Y  Q  R  R  E  M
H  I  V  E  I  F  J  N  Y  T  D  M  U  I
```

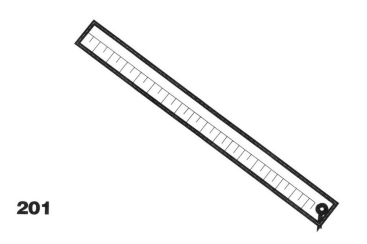

Insects

APHID

BEETLE

BLOWFLY

BORER

BRISTLETAIL

BUTTERFLY

CHIGGER

COCKROACH

CRICKET

FIREFLY

FLEA

GADFLY

GLOWWORM

GNAT

HORNET

KATYDID

LADYBUG

LOCUST

LOUSE

MEALWORM

MEALYBUG

SILVERFISH

TERMITE

WASP

```
N T F Z G M E A L W O R M Q
Y S H N T E R M I T E R T J
M L A D Y B U G E B O Q X F
A T F L E A A K M W T S G C
C M V E S U C Q W I J U H E
P Y T I R I Y O Y A B I M C
C L S I R I L L P Y G D W O
E F U C X G F V L G D O E C
C D C H O W R A E I P F S K
O A O B O R E R D R D S U R
Q G L L Z M T Y T N F K O O
T I B R I S T L E T A I L A
E D I H P A U W A S P U S C
G K Z C K N B U T E N R O H
```

203

Sharks

ANGEL

BANJO

BASKING

BLACKFIN

BULLHEAD

DOGFISH

ELFIN

FRILLED

GREAT WHITE

GREY

GROUND

GUITAR

HAMMERHEAD

HORNED

LEMON

LEOPARD

MAKO

NURSE

SAND

SILKY

THRESHER

TIGER

TOPE

ZEBRA

```
U Z B D E N R O H P R M Z U
O P Z N O D L E G N A G G N
T S B M V G J H Z K T N R N
L I E P O T F M O M I Y E H
U L G O L J T I P K U S A S
T K Z E M B N H S Q G M T S
P Y E S R U N A R H M H W H
V D B Z X L B B B E M S H G
X U R D E L L I R F S F I W
H Q A L N H C H N Y Q H T Y
Y D F E S E E D R A P O E L
N I F K C A L B E G T R K R
N J B E D D N U O R G Y X V
W X J K F Q Q D A E O W X N
```

205

Mammals

ANTELOPE	LEOPARD
BADGER	LION
BEAR	LLAMA
BEAVER	MOOSE
BUFFALO	PLATYPUS
BULL	POSSUM
CAMEL	RABBIT
DONKEY	REINDEER
ELEPHANT	SHEEP
FERRET	SKUNK
GIRAFFE	TIGER
HORSE	WOLF
JAGUARUNDI	ZEBRA

R	P	P	A	J	X	S	X	A	D	Z	Q	M	N
E	E	L	E	Q	K	U	F	F	U	I	W	D	B
G	E	I	A	U	R	A	B	B	I	T	C	W	A
I	H	L	N	T	Y	E	F	F	A	R	I	G	O
T	S	K	T	D	Y	J	V	S	M	D	D	C	T
C	A	M	E	L	E	P	H	A	N	T	G	Y	E
B	U	L	L	S	E	E	U	U	E	M	P	E	R
J	U	A	O	A	H	O	R	S	E	B	R	K	R
H	M	O	P	M	J	A	P	D	E	P	F	N	E
A	M	Q	E	B	U	F	F	A	L	O	V	O	F
Y	X	W	A	G	J	S	R	C	R	I	W	D	I
L	A	L	A	I	O	B	S	X	E	D	O	T	V
P	A	J	E	Q	E	U	E	O	C	J	L	N	P
S	K	T	S	Z	K	J	R	M	P	R	F	K	E

207

Wild Cats

BAY CAT

BOBCAT

CARACAL

CHEETAH

COUGAR

IRIOMOTE

JAGUAR

JUNGLE

KELLAS

KODKOD

LION

LYNX

MARGAY

OCELOT

PAMPAS

PANTHER

PUMA

SAND

SERVAL

SMILODON

SNOW LEOPARD

TIGER

TSHUSHIMA

```
Q H V L H Y C Y S A P M A P
K Y O F Y O X O A A B F I C
Y O O C U G J U N G L E Y D
Y F D G G Z K T O T R L N E
A A A K G H H Y D S T A E C
D R A P O E L W O N S V M K
E A L T R D T O L D H R Z F
P U M A W C C O I A U E I R
L G A C C E H G M R S S E E
F A N B L A P E S O H G N W
U J I O Y U R M E S I N G O
K O T B I U E A C T M R T N
E A X N Y L T A C Y A B I Z
C Q S K E V Z M A N D H S L
```

209

Mythical Creatures

CACUS	HYDRA
CALIBAN	LADON
CENTAUR	MEDUSA
CERBERUS	MERMAID
CETO	MINOTAUR
CYCLOPS	PEGASUS
DRAGON	SPHINX
ECHIDNA	TALOS
GIGANTES	TYPHOEUS
GORGON	VAMPIRE
GRENDEL	WEREWOLF
GRIFFIN	ZOMBIE

T G V X N I H P S D C C G V
A Y F Z O M B I E B E C L A
L N P F G S W K P T E G K M
O K Z H R U A T O N I M H P
S I S U O R O C T G C B N I
S C W K G E G A A L X B M R
D A U E Y B U N L A I E E C
G I P V R R T S O N I C R C
H L E D N E R G D G S B M C
Y D G R S C W I A U A H A C
D U A R A O H O L G J R I N
R N S C A C Y C L O P S D E
A S U D E M G R I F F I N A
U S S A A L J G D R Y Y Q F

211

Academy Awards

ACTING	MAKEUP
ACTOR	NOMINEE
ACTRESS	OSCAR
ANIMATED	PICTURE
ANNUAL	SCORE
CINEMA	SCREENPLAY
COSTUMES	SHORT FILM
DIRECTING	SONG
DOCUMENTARY	SOUND
EDITING	SUNDAY
FASHION	VISUAL
FOREIGN	WINNER

```
Y N O M I N E E G U A D C Q
J R B T X D W I N N E R S C
L T A V I S U A L R I H J N
J S H T A C A N I M A T E D
W U I X N R P V G L Q C C K
G N I T C E R I D I D J S A
G D B N O E M U C F E S S O
D A B J S N R U X T E R C K
M Y M O T P O Q C R U N O E
V G M V U L T I T O O R R F
C I N E M A C C H H D N E H
L U K O E Y A X A S O U N D
M A V K S B A N N U A L Z U
M G U G F Q Y K T G O F S K
```

213

At the Movies

ACTION

AISLES

AUDIENCE

CANDY

CHOCOLATE

CINEMA

COMEDY

CREDITS

DOLBY

DRAMA

HORROR

LINE

POPCORN

PROJECTOR

ROMANCE

ROWS

SCREEN

SEATS

SODA

STRAW

STUB

SUSPENSE

THRILLER

TICKET

```
N E T A L O C O H C M P Z Y
J V N K S I Y B V Q Z A J U
Q Z I T N B F G U E C U A A
L F R E L L I R H T K C M H
G A M O C R E D I T S A J C
W A D B T A S O D A R F F F
U H W T E C N E I D U A N J
R O M A N C E D B L L I N E
N R O C P O P J Y R P S Y F
E R I L J M S M O F C L T N
J O Q I S E U W K R X E R V
Z R U V A D S B E J P S G V
R M D T W Y T E K C I T H G
P I S Z B B N C V P A C W D
```

215

Musical Instruments

ACCORDION

BAGPIPES

BANJO

BASSOON

CARILLON

CLAVICHORD

CONCERTINA

DOUMBEK

DULCIMER

FIDDLE

FLUTE

GUITAR

HARPSICHORD

KEYBOARD

MANDOLIN

OBOE

ORGAN

PIANO

RECORDER

SYNTHESIZER

TIMPANI

TRUMPET

UKULELE

VIOLIN

```
E H T D O U M B E K X Y C C
L A Y E R E L E L U K U P D
D P I A N O E P K B T J D W
D W S Y N T H E S I Z E R N
I J K W U I Y C I E O B O B
F U O L G B T N I T G O H A
C M F R O U A R A S S B C N
T A B A G P I P E S P C I J
E N R P M A O T A C O R V O
P D T I G O N B A R N T A S
M O T U L U Z T D R Z O L H
U L J D U L C I M E R B C A
R I R E D R O C E R H G E Q
T N C O L N I N I L O I V O
```

217

Art & Entertainment Magazines

ARTWEEK

AUDIO

BIOGRAPHY

COVER

DETAILS

GOLDMINE

INDEX

INTERVIEW

LAUNCH

NEW YORK

NOTORIOUS

PAPER

PEOPLE

PHOTOGRAPHIC

PREMIERE

ROLLING STONE

SMART TV

SPIN

STRINGS

TALK

TV GUIDE

US MAGAZINE

VARIETY

VIBE

```
R R J X P I V N O E B G A O
N O T O R I O U S B O I R V
Y L L Y E C R P P L U B T T
E T R L M C I C D S I T W A
D L E A I N B M M O R I E L
E K P I E N I A G A I N E K
T K A O R N G R M E Y D K N
A R P X E A A S L S I E U O
I O H I Z P V I T U K X S A
L Y C I H P A R G O T O H P
S W N Y E B I V E C N O U R
P E U C I N T E R V I E W D
V N A U G S Y L L I O Y Q P
H D L S R J Z P K W T C H Q
```

219

Newspapers

ADVERTISEMENTS

ARTS

BUSINESS

DELIVERY

EDITOR

FASHION

INFORMATION

INTERNATIONAL

LOCAL

NATIONAL

NEWS

PAPER

PRESS

PRINT

REAL ESTATE

RECYCLE

REPORT

SCIENCE

SECTION

SPORTS

STOCKS

TIMES

WEATHER

WRITER

A C J P A H W O N Q N T B E
Y D D A R J D F R E I H H D A
T D V O R F S Y W M E I F A N
I Q E E W T X S E C T I O N N
C S P L R D S S T O A I I U P
L A N O I T A N R E T N I T
P W P C T V I D G A S R O R
W E P A E X E S M S E G W U
R S T L R R C R E C L E S S
I F A S H I O N Y M A S P K
H Z U D E F I C A T E Y O C
N O H N N S L J H R R N R O
M I C I U E V E P R I N T T
O E W B L K R C L V A R S S

THE WALL STREET

221

Sports Magazines

ALASKA

BACKPACKER

BICYCLING

BIG BROTHER

BLUE

BOATING

BRAKE

DAILY BREAD

DISCOVER

ESPN

FREEZE

GOLF TIPS

IYF HOCKEY

LEVEL TEN

OUTSIDE

POWDER

SAILING

SKIING

SLAM

SNAP

SPORT

STRENGTH

TRANSWORLD

WARP

R X A S P I T F L O G T B V
E M L E V E L T E N Y I O Y
Q Q A O B O A T I N G T S B
B Q S F D A I L Y B R E A D
E R K M V T C E R O R C I L
D X A L Y Y Z O P E K J L R
I L V K C E T S D P H Q I O
S U Q I E H K W A E R M N W
T I B R E V O C S I D H G S
U L F R E P K P O P A N S N
O U S T R E N G T H I Y O A
H P G A R H U D A I F V D R
V G W M F C O L K W D Y N T
E W J U B A H S B Q Z H I O

Fashion & Style Magazines

ALLURE

CLARITY

CODE

DETAILS

ELLE

ESQUIRE

ESSENCE

GEAR

GENRE

GLAMOUR

LATIN GIRL

MADEMOISELLE

MAXIM

MIRABELLA

MORE

NEW MAN

NEW WOMAN

PAPER

SEVENTEEN

SHAPE

SOURCE

TALK

TEEN

VOGUE

```
B L S M U J Q G W P J V C E
K P D N A M W E N A M O R E E
B J Y T A L K N E P D S S E E
L N J U S N L R F E Y Q X X
H A Y I E I K E C R U O S K
B M T J V J E L B I F A L S
Y O I I E Z V I R A P S J Z
V W R E N J D E U T R L S U
D W A H T G S W O Q U I Q I
I E L L E S I O M E D A M M
R N C I E P M R A P G T I N
D A L N N F A L L U R E X Q
N N C D N Z E H G B C D A C
H E U G O V J X S D M D M R
```

225

Bonus Puzzle By Mark Danna

SUITS ME FINE

A deck of cards has four suits: clubs (♣), diamonds (♦), hearts (♥), and spades (♠). The symbols for these suits appear in the grid in place of the words for suits in the word list. For example, CLUB SODA would appear as ♣SODA.

```
♥  T  O  ♥  T  A  L  K  S  ♠  A
M  E  ♠  ♣  G  A  P  V  W  E  ♠
A  B  V  S  ♦  R  U  O  I  A  N
♣  A  M  A  R  D  R  G  ♠  R  T
Y  S  O  N  R  K  P  A  H  I  I
R  E  S  D  S  B  L  S  W  Z  ♥
T  B  E  W  E  L  E  T  ♠  O  ♥
N  A  A  I  A  ♠  ♥  T  F  N  T
U  L  ♣  C  ♦  H  D  G  E  A  I
O  L  N  H  I  H  O  I  G  ♦  H
C  ♦  E  G  O  L  F  ♣  V  B  T
♣  A  F  P  D  U  ♥  E  K  A  T
D  O  E  R  A  ♣  S  S  T  C  D
E  ♦  J  U  B  I  L  E  E  K  A
K  B  R  E  A  K  O  N  E  S  ♥
```

ARIZONA DIAMONDBACKS
BASEBALL DIAMOND
BRAVEHEART
BREAK ONE'S HEART
CALL A SPADE A SPADE
CLUBHOUSE
CLUB SANDWICH
COUNTRY CLUB
DAVID SPADE
DIAMOND HEAD

DIAMOND JUBILEE
DRAMA CLUB
GOLF CLUB
HEART OF GOLD
HEART-TO-HEART TALK
HOPE DIAMOND
IN SPADES
PURPLE HEART
SPADEWORK
TAKE HEART

Answer Keys

for the puzzles on pages 2-227

Page 4: Card Games

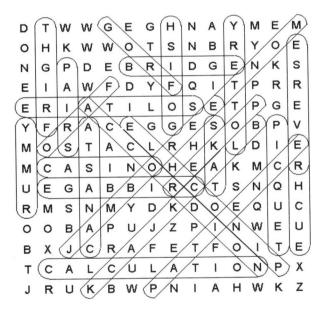

Page 6: Transportation

Page 8: Things That Fly

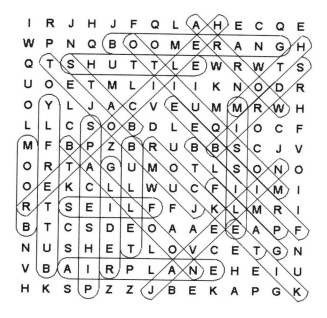

Page 10: Space

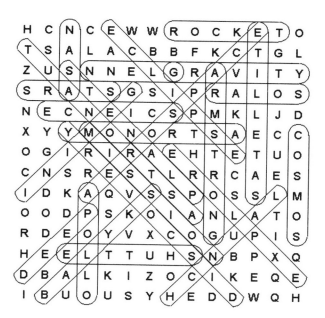

Page 12: Airplane Parts

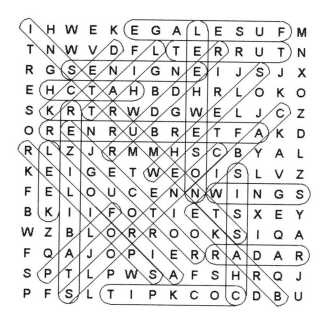

Page 14: Boats

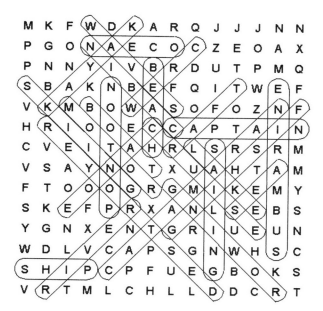

Page 16: Airports

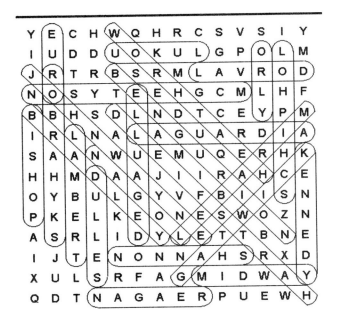

Page 18: Car Parts

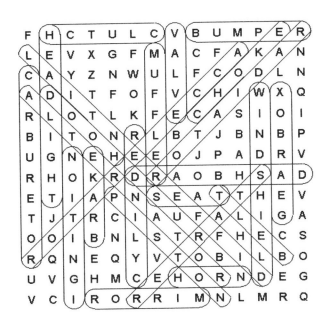

Page 20: Car Racing

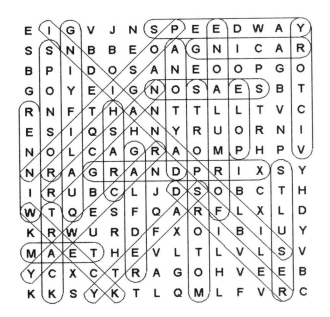

Page 22: Countries of Africa

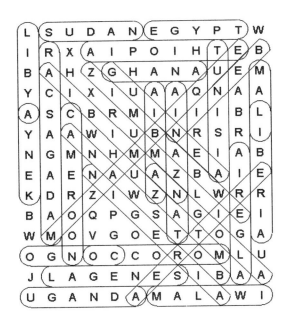

Page 24: Animals of Africa

Page 26: Animals of Australia

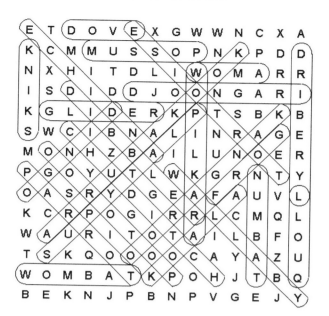

Page 28: Cities and Towns of Australia

Page 30: Birds of North America

Page 38: Mexico

Page 34: Capitals of Europe

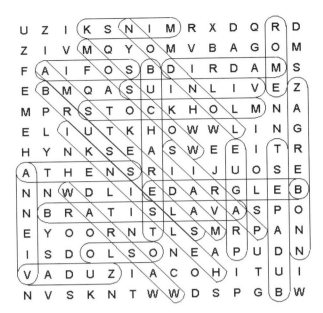

Page 36: Scandanavia

Page 38: Spain

Page 40: Switzerland

Page 42: France

Page 44: Greece

Page 46: Italy

Page 48: Capitals of States & Provinces

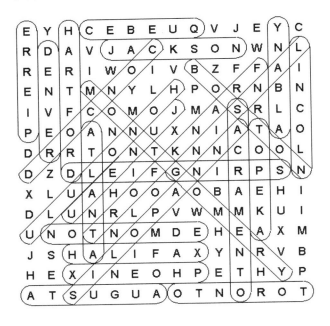

Page 50: Caribbean & the West Indies

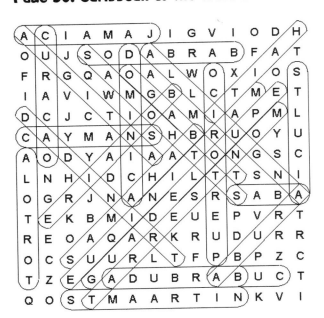

Page 52: Egypt

Page 54: Languages

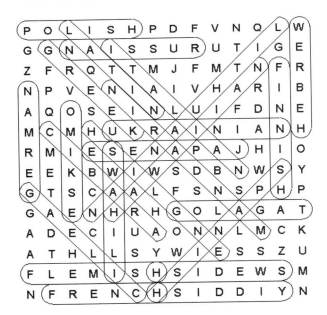

Page 56: Languages of Asia

Page 58: Fish

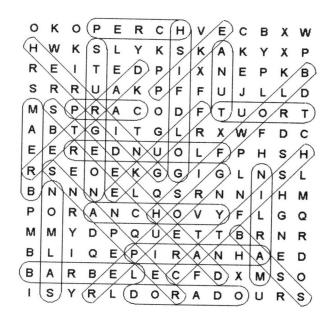

Page 60: Wild West

Page 62: Oceania

Page 64: Basketball Players

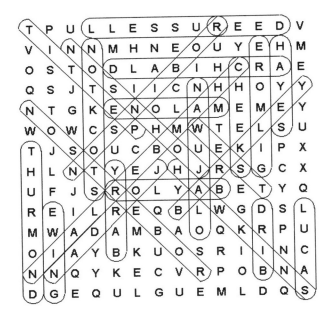

Page 66: Baseball

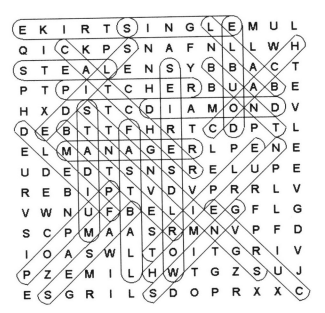

Page 68: Basketball

Page 70: Bowling

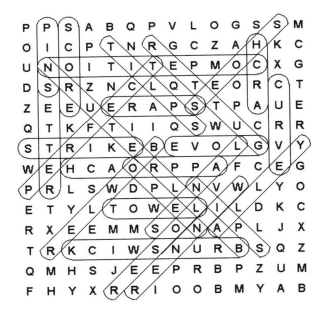

Page 72: Football

Page 74: Golf

Page 76: Martial Arts

Page 78: Emmy Awards

Page 80: Famous Actors

Page 82: Famous Actresses

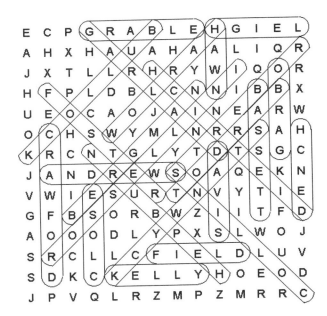

Page 84: Skiing

Page 86: Tennis

238

Page 88: Track and Field

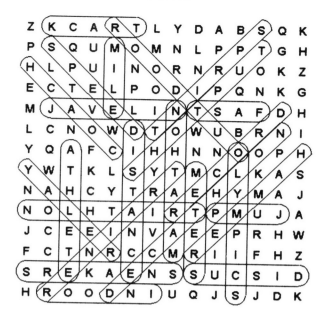

Page 90: Artist

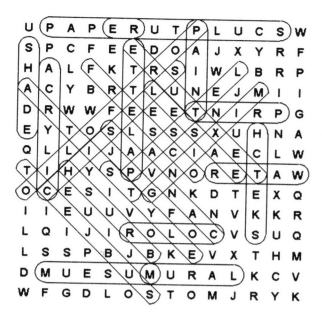

Page 92: Beach

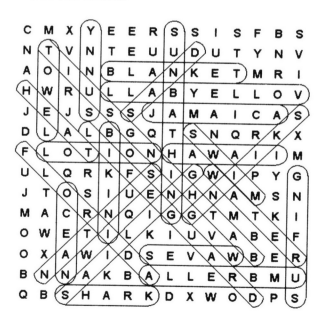

Page 94: Camp

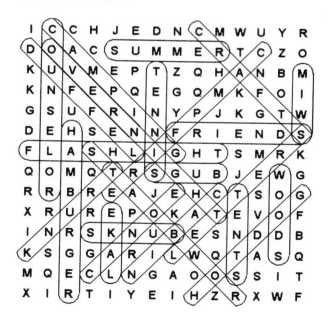

Page 96: Classic Books

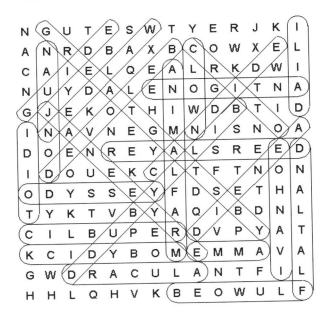

Page 98: Collectibles

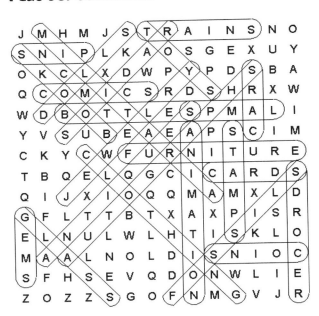

Page 100: Evening News

Page 102: Exercise

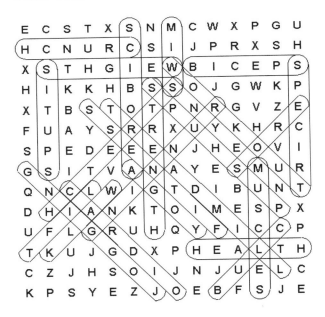

Page 104: Fishing

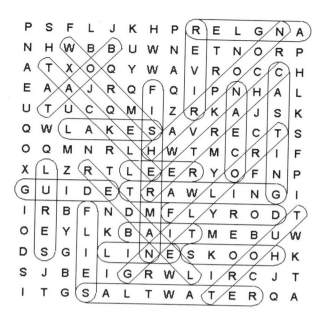

Page 106: Music

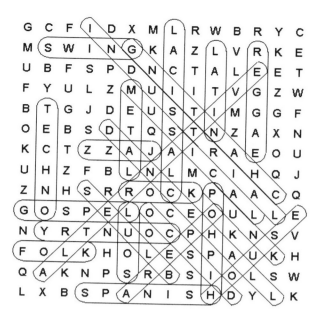

Page 108: Photography

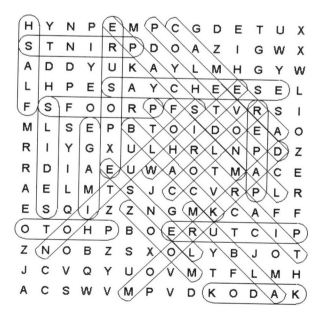

Page 110: Slumber Party

Page 112: That's Sharp

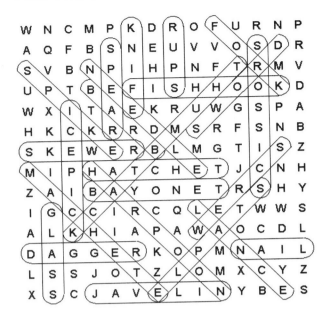

Page 114: Tools

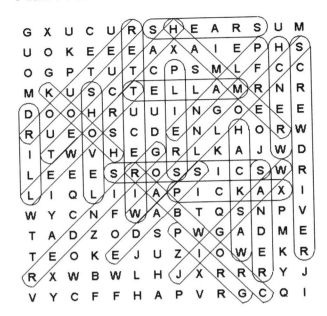

Page 116: Dance

Page 118: Fabric

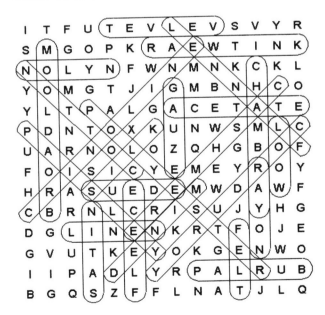

Page 120: Green

Page 122: Red

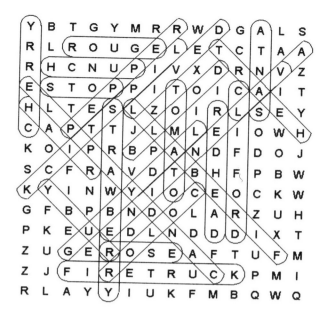

Page 124: Halloween

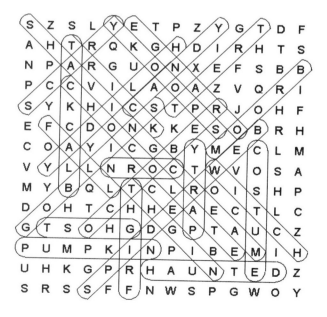

Page 126: Thanksgiving

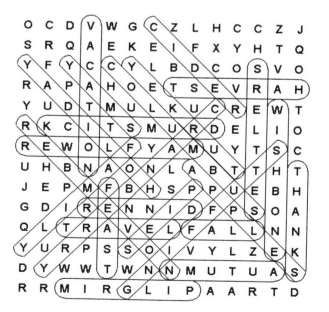

Page 128: Christmas

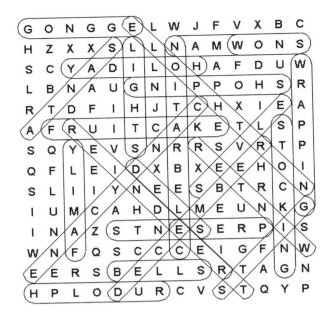

Page 130: Valentine's Day

Page 132: Fourth of July

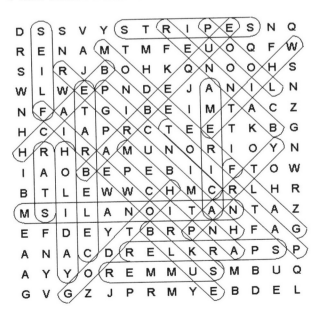

Page 134: Anybody Thirsty?

Page 136: Barbecue

Page 138: Bread

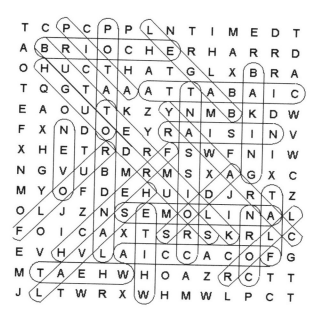

Page 140: Breakfast

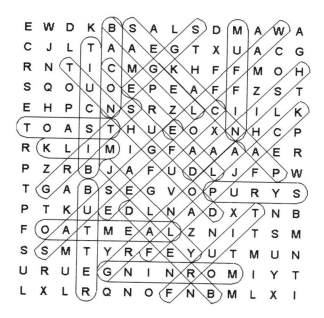

Page 142: Desserts

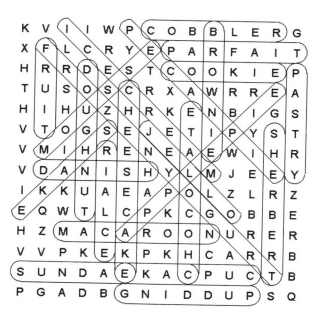

245

Page 144: Pies

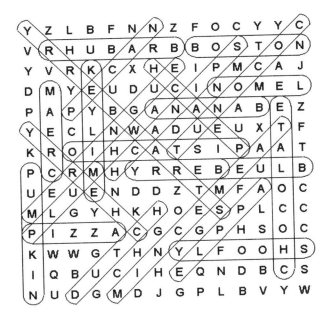

Page 146: Sundaes

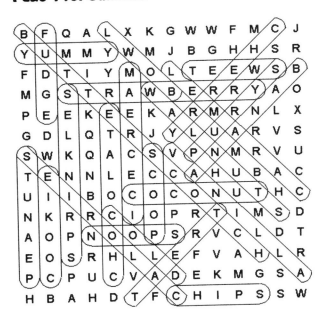

Page 148: Diner Food

Page 150: Fruit

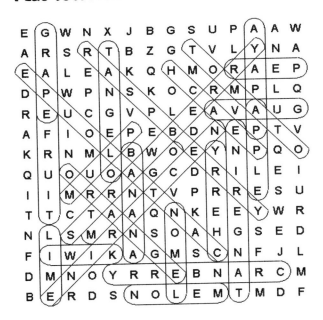

Page 152: Herbs

Page 154: Nuts

Page 156: Vegetables

Page 158: What's on the Table?

Page 160: In the Bathroom

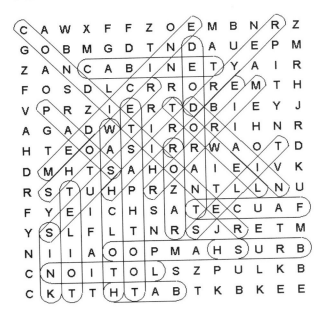

Page 162: In the Bedroom

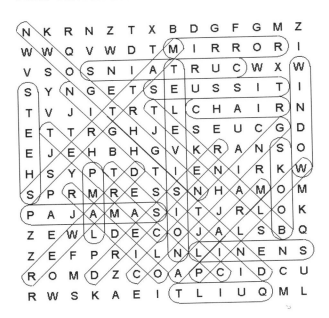

Page 164: Get Dressed

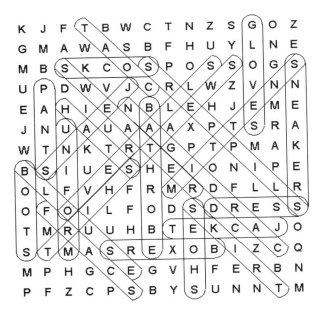

Page 166: Gems

Page 168: In the Kitchen

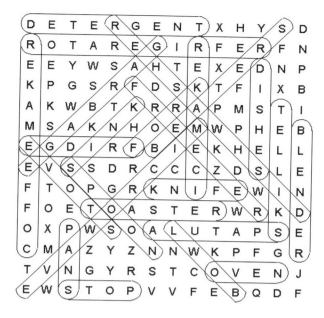

Page 170: It's Cold

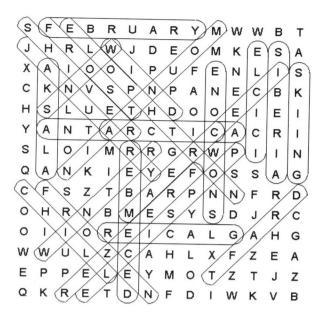

Page 172: It's Hot

Page 174: Jewelry

Page 176: Clean Up

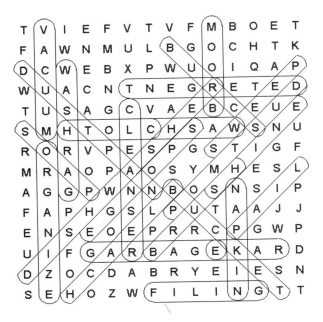

Page 178: In the Living Room

Page 180: Family

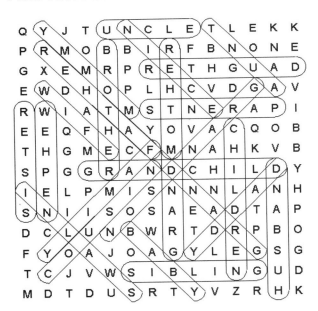

Page 182: Flowers

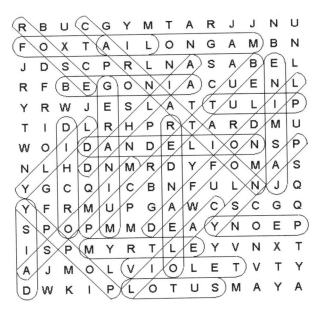

Page 184: Garden

Page 186: School Time

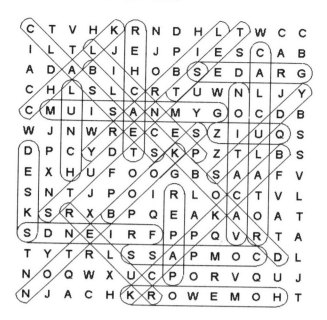

Page 188: Begins with "cla"

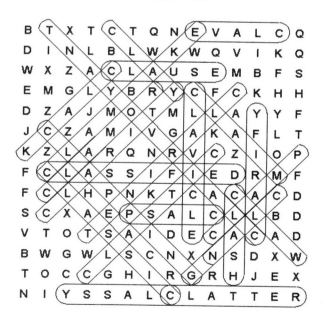

Page 190: Begins with "gra"

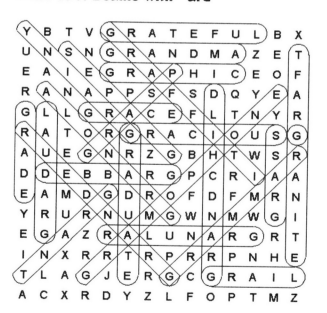

Page 192: Begins with "pla"

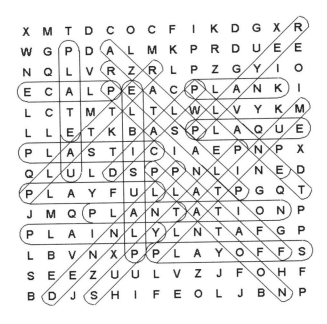

Page 194: Presidents of the US

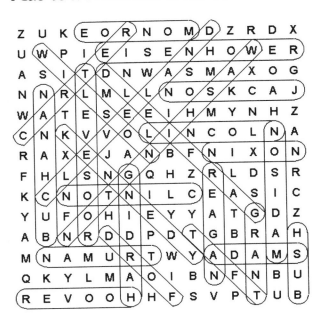

Page 196: Trees

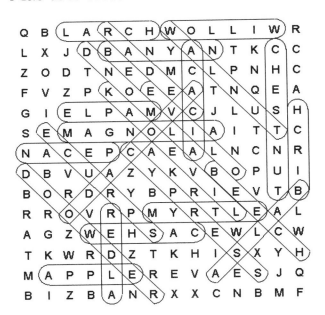

Page 198: Constellations

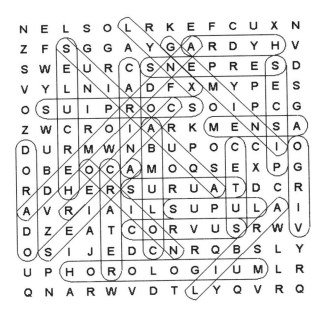

Page 200: Measurements

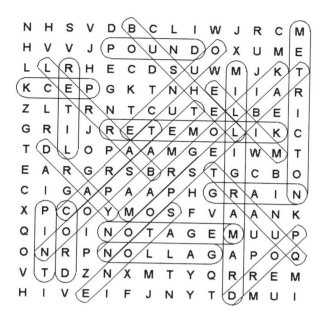

Page 202: Insects

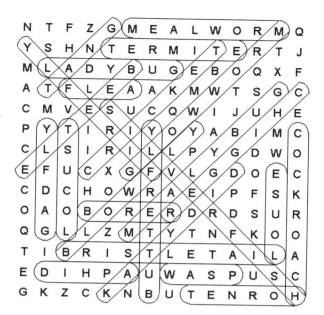

Page 204: Sharks

Page 206: Mammals

Page 208: Wild Cats

Page 210: Mythical Creatures

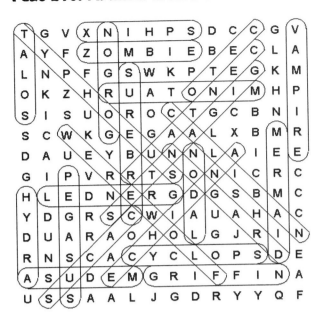

Page 212: Academy Awards

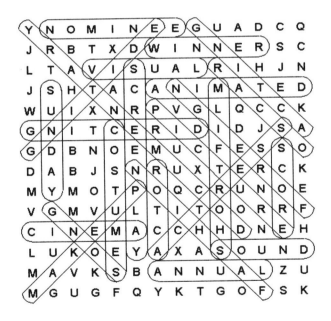

Page 214: At the Movies

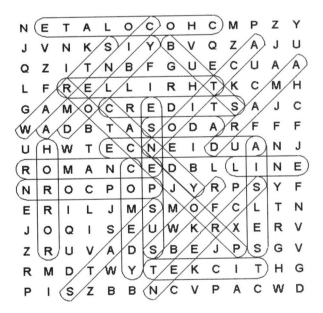

Page 216: Musical Instruments

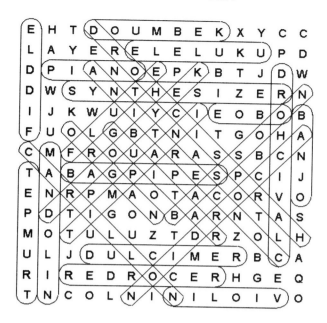

Page 218: Art & Entertainment Magazines

Page 220: Newspapers

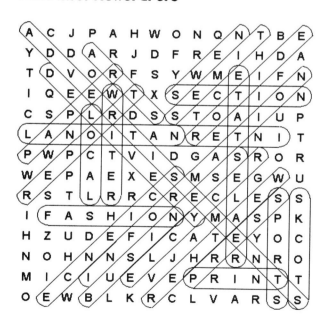

Page 222: Sports Magazines

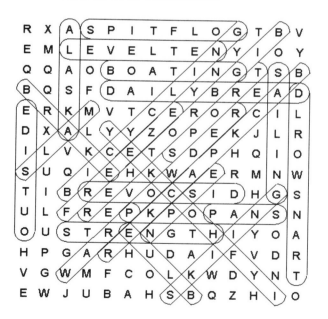

255

Page 224: Fashion & Style Magaziness

```
B L S M U J Q G W P J V C E
K P D N A M W E N A M O R E
B J Y T A L K N E P D S S E
L N J U S N L R F E Y Q X X
H A Y I E I K E C R U O S K
B M T J V J E L B I F A L S
Y O I I E Z V I R A P S J Z
V W R E N J D E U T R L S U
D W A H T G S W O Q U I Q I
I E L L E S I O M E D A M M
R N C I E P M R A P G T I N
D A L N N F A L L U R E X Q
N N C D N Z E H G B C D A C
H E U G O V J X S D M D M R
```

Page 227: SUITS ME FINE

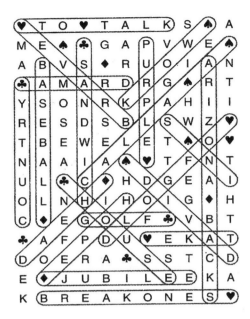

Sam Spade gave a diamond ring to his sweetheart
at the nightclub for a club steak.